Yvonne Cullen was born in Dublin in 1966. She studied Law and was called to the Bar in Dublin in 1990 (she has not practised). She lives in Dublin where she divides her time between writing, teaching creative writing, and playing music. She won the American Ireland Fund Prize at Listowel in 1997 for "Invitation to the Air" (Poems) Italics Press 1998. Her poetry has been widely praised and anthologised, most recently in "The New Irish Poets," (Bloodaxe Books, 2004, Editor Selina Guinness). She is a regular tutor for the Irish Writers' Centre and Poetry Ireland, among other organisations, and her style of facilitation has also won praise. Together with Nicole Rourke, she runs the facilitation partnership CreativityWorks Ireland. At the moment her favourite quote is from poet Tomas Tranströmer who lists what he will get around to "One day when I am dead and can at last concentrate." In the meantime, and actually in no hurry at all to arrive at Mr Tranströmer's ideal work situation, she is finishing a second collection of poems, and working on a number of other prose, screen and music projects.

ALL GOOD THINGS BEGIN

Cover design by Conor Ferguson
Typesetting and design Ian Cahill
Printed in Ireland by Colour Books

ISBN 0-9554262-0-0
ISBN 978-0-9554262-0-9

ALL GOOD THINGS BEGIN

Edited by Yvonne Cullen

offcentre | publishing

Contents

Foreword

With Work

In Love

At Home

Outdoors

Elsewhere

On the Way

Foreword

This book was conceived as a showcase for the forty-two writers included here, all of whose work I first heard over the last year and a half, in writers' workshops at the Irish Writers' Centre in Dublin. Almost all of the work here was written while these writers were attending my workshops, with our meetings acting as a production deadline for them. So far, so usual, as far as Creative Writing workshops go!

What has been very far from usual has been the writing.

So much work of such quality gathers here – as you'll soon see, reader – that I have to stop now and comment on the lovely fluke that collected these writers, gave them to me as workshop participants and gave them the awareness of their talent that made this book seem the appropriate next step. For me, personally, this book-which-began-as-a-showcase has come to seem more like a jukebox of favourite songs as I've been putting it together: a record of the voices of this once-off group of writers .

They are all well on their creative way now, these writers, with bigger projects in place; with publications and praise starting to roll in, for some, and places on the university creative writing MA programmes for others. And what was conceived as a showcase for new voices also comes now to seem more and more like a fanfare for accomplished and achieved ones – to use similes from the season ahead in which we hope this book will sell out: a box-full of nothing but great chocolates; a CD full of hits!

To you in the bookshop, browsing now: buy this! Give yourself or someone else a treat, and these writers the readers and encouragement they deserve – and watch out for their names down the line. If you're not sure, read a few pages at random. And if you should still need another reason to buy: the profits from sale of ALL GOOD THINGS BEGIN will be used as follows: a donation to fund Creative Writing workshops at Dublin Adult Learning Centre; a scholarship fund to support young writers from our workshops who are taking time off work to study writing at university level; and a fund to allow for a similar anthology from these workshops next year. You can keep up to date with Off Centre Publishing's activities at www.offcentrepublishing.com.

Lastly, to the writers: it's been an unforgettable pleasure working with you: hearing all of this work brand new; watching the camaraderie and support grow in the groups represented here: the Tuesday night, Wednesday and Thursday afternoon and night classes at the IWC.

In a year and a half we've gone from being groups of strangers trying to take in each other's faces and names in bright classrooms in Parnell Square, to colleagues in this project. You've also become some of the most honest, supportive and rigorous critics of each others' writing. And beyond all this, despite the seriousness of the mission to fulfil your writing potential, we've also never let a chance to laugh pass us by.

I feel I've been on an adventure with you all. It turned out to be both a literary Croagh Patrick: gathering and editing and showing to best effect the work of 42 writers; and a joy because of your talent and your ambition. As your editor, I also feel it's a coup to be getting to present in one book so many exciting voices. For now, they still seem to belong together and one of the beauties of this book is that fact that it will always hold your work in this good company, no matter where else it goes from here. My adventure ends in these days: days like last Friday, when I held this manuscript on my lap while waiting outside a Dawson Street café to meet some of you; a September day roughly a year after this book was first talked about. The next leg of the adventure is yours, the book's, and the reader's. Enjoy it, all of you.

Yvonne Cullen
Dublin
October 2006

all
good things
begin

with work

Ribbons and Ropes

Marcella Morgan

In the moments before they first saw each other, he was standing outside her front door, with his suitcase, and his finger on the doorbell. She was in the hall on her way from the living room to the kitchen. When he pressed the doorbell she happened to be right beside the front door and she opened it immediately. This surprised him. It surprised him so much that he lost his balance and fell against the railings with his suitcase swinging out away from him in his left hand.

And that was how she first saw him: on the ground outside her front door, his arms thrown wide open, one hand clinging to the top of the railing and his other hand gripping the suitcase that had swung away from him. He looked terrified and she bent down immediately beside him and with her hands out towards him, but not touching him, she asked, "Are you okay?" And that was how he first saw her.

He seemed to her to be a fragile person. She invited him into her house and made him some tea to comfort him. He sat on her sofa. He liked her home. She sat on the sofa beside him, turned slightly away from him, giving him only a side view of her face and sometimes only a curve of cheek, her eyes hidden away completely. He never once grabbed her face and demanded she look at him straight. He accepted what view she offered, sitting back on her sofa. He absorbed the room. His attention pulled his eyes around like an excited child who wanted to show him everything and everything he saw there filled him with peace.

He opened his suitcase. He offered her the things he had brought with him. His audacity made it easy for her to say, "I do not want your wares. I need nothing."

His suitcase was a big brown one. The edges were sharp right angles and the lid closed down square on them. It had many compartments filled with different kinds of things and as she looked over them colours and glints caught her eye. He took out some small objects but she refused to touch them. She sat with her hands in her lap and she shook her head. Then he leaned down and heavily lifted the whole top shelf of compartments out of the suitcase and under that there lay what looked like a tangled mass of guts.

"These" he declared, "are my ribbons and my ropes. I have come today to sell you my ribbons and my ropes." She laughed. She had never seen ribbons and ropes tangled up like that in the bottom of a suitcase before. She held her hands palms together before her mouth. "Come!" he said standing up and motioning her to do the same. She refused to stand. He took her hands and he pulled her from the sofa. She stumbled a little against him and she laughed with her face turned down towards the suitcase of tangles. He bent down and drove a hand into the suitcase and out he pulled a long thin white ribbon as easy as if he'd been sucking up pasta from a bowl.

He positioned her about three feet directly in front of him. She stood there like an audience member on stage. He threw out the ribbon, holding one end as the other curved out and around to the right. She watched it as it slowly curved behind her. When she could turn her head no more she flipped her head back around to the left to see it emerge from her other side and float on into his other hand. They stood there like that, with the ribbon suspended in the air and filling the entire room with a giant arc, with her in the centre. He smiled as he began to draw in the ends of the ribbon until the arc eventually closed in on her, the ribbon pressed against her back and her bare arms. She stood and smiled at him. "Come here," he said. She said, "No." He pulled on the ends of the ribbon and she felt a band of pressure along her back and bare arms. She did not move towards him. Suddenly he released one end of the ribbon and it slid around her back and from her bare arms and suddenly the band of pressure was gone and the ribbon was bundled in his hands. She felt briefly unstable. She steadied herself and then she smiled.

The Caretaker of Horology

(Ruth Belville, Spinster & London's last time carrier, 1853 –1943)

Helena Nolan

We wear time lightly like a bracelet
But then you carried it
Precious as a baby
In a large black bag
– So much your father's
Then your mother's daughter
The dedication of a veritable Ruth –
First to check its veracity
With the Astronomer Royal
His great brow brought to
Bear upon your skirts
Rising and falling like the sea
Against his polished floors
His great doors open
Only to you
Disgruntled men in the corridors
Muttering vile
And unforgivable slander
Of your "womanly charms"
As you swept past on a wave
Of crinoline and velvet
Your face dormant within your bonnet
Their eyes slitted with greed
Watching the time
You bore within its case
A chronometer of some weight
Pulling your arms like chains
Then off you sailed relentless
On your Monday morning voyage
To the bankers and the merchants
Touting your wares
Among the houses of repute
Who must demand

Only the best quality of time
Fresh from Greenwich
To their corridors of power
No sundial pastoral for them
They watch the hands idle on the faces
And wait for the lady bearer of the time
Your warm hands on the cold instrument
A breath of life in the machine
Now we say regular as clockwork
Yours was a regular industry of chimes
Homespun resisting all the other claims
A tender fostering
And still you came for year on year on year
Past withered chances, bitterness and shame
Past radio pips that marched out towards your fate
Until science overtook you on the path
Until aged eight lone decades and a half
Like a tight-wound
Clock, you stopped.

One for the Road

Joe Walsh

Kevin grimaced, hissed cold air through the side of his mouth and ignored the short-handled axe tucked neatly inside his customer's denim jacket. He lifted two pint glasses, shoved them under the Guinness taps and pulled hard on the handles.

"You're a kind man," said the tall tinker, as he ran his rough hand along the glimmering, dark mahogany bar top. He gazed in mock wonderment at the five polished brass pillars that reached up to the white ceiling. Kevin and the tinker had the lounge to themselves.

The tinker allowed the groaning burden of his posterior to rest into a leather-topped barstool. Behind him low seating ran along the wall, separated by wooden panels that would allow whispering couples to snuggle or squabble in relative intimacy. Beneath him flecks of wool from the rich red carpet twinkled in the warm light. The smell of carpet shampoo lingered. Three elaborate candelabra-style chandeliers reflected out from the gold-framed mirrors behind the bar. From everywhere Christmas tinsel hung. Being St Stephen's Day, the tinsel was well tattered.

"Sparkling like a whore's handbag," said the tinker, but he smiled amiably and licked his lips.

Behind the bar, Kevin grimaced again. Tiny sweat stains appeared on the breast of his white shirt, as though the pulling of pints was a manly task. He lit a Major and as he sucked deeply, the tinker's short, shifty-looking companion swaggered in from the hall. He looked like a mongrel with a permanent grievance. He didn't smile at all.

Kevin reached to top up one of the unfinished pints. Black stout swirled into brown and pushed the creamy head to the top of the glass while the smell of burnt hops invaded his senses, soothing his nerves.

Thirst, verging on desperation, shone in his customers' moist eyes and swollen mouths. He set the pints down at a distance from the men. To let them settle. Both customers and pints. The Guinness was good here and deserved such respect. The old desire lingered but his interest was strictly professional these days.

He presented the pints and they were lifted and lowered in large creamy gulps.

Pausing only to belch, the big man said: "I suppose we'll have another." He looked a little too settled for Kevin's liking. His companion disdainfully examined the elaborate furnishings and said: "You won't starve, anyway."

"Or die of thirst either," said Kevin, reminding them of his act of kindness in leaving them in, on a day when most bars were shut to tinkers and settled folks alike. He had found them standing there when he opened the great oak door to let the cold wind air his dusty hallways.

At first he refused them but the big man had spoken gently, pleading: "The thirst is killing us. A quick pint and we're gone before the dregs have fallen."

Kevin had been wary; the hotel was supposed to be shut for two days, with him as sole caretaker. And the monastic solitude it had offered was his sanctuary against the frazzling terror that is Christmas. But they looked frozen and dishevelled and Kevin was not the kind of man who would turn two strangers out on the Feast of Stephen.

He would give them two more pints and that would be it. "It's a bitter day out there," he said, conversationally, raising two more glasses to the pumps.

"Like a woman's heart," said the big tinker. He grinned again as he caught a sympathetic flash in Kevin's eye. Kevin averted his gaze to the frosty window. Outside, the trees were raw from winter. They stretched up like giant insect legs from sleet-capped gravel, and the grey wall at the end of the courtyard blended into the grey noon sky. The courtyard was empty now, except for a mini tractor tied to a trailer that held two huge water barrels. They had been standing there since summer. The builders had used the barrels as bins and, over the months, they had been filled almost to the brim with rainwater and rubbish. Kevin had promised his boss that, during the shutdown – when no one was looking – he would drive the water wagon down to the main road and dump the contents in a ditch.

"And one for yourself," said the big man.

Kevin laughed. "No. Not any more," he said.

"Well I suppose we'll have two small ones."

Kevin hesitated.

"To take the bite out of the icy cold; we'll be listening to wren boys all afternoon."

Kevin laughed.

"Powers?"

They both nodded.

The strong whiskey scent as he poured brought back guilt-edged memories of wilder, younger days. Powers had always been his own favourite – neat. They had tried to woo him with smooth Glenfiddich when he trained in The Dorchester in London, and with Jack Daniel's when he ran Maura's Irish Bar under the boulevard in Queens, but the first had no bite and the second reminded him of the golden syrup his mother used to put on his bread, pretending it was honey. Powers, sharp and warm, was first his invigorating temptress, then his nightly tipple – and finally his morning medicine.

Those days were gone now.

Kevin handed up the whiskeys and pints, and sank to his hunkers to load Britvic bottles from a case onto the lower shelves.

And take stock.

Four months earlier, he had walked out the gate of St Malachi's clinic with nothing in his pocket but a cancelled Visa card and a social welfare contact number. In the space of two years he had managed to lose his wife Linda, his three sons, thirty thousand pounds and the need to knock back two large ones in an early house before work. He was broke and alone, but dry. He hid away in his basement flat off Portobello for three of those months; drawing the dole, backing horses and pretending to scour the vacancies ads. Eventually, one early December day, when the Rathmines Christmas frenzy was playing jingle jangle with his nerves, he looked up the number of his old boss Pete Nugent, a man with a hard edge and a harder centre. Kevin had worked for Pete on and off over the years. He was the only man he could turn to. If Pete wouldn't hire him, nobody would.

After three days of indecision Kevin eventually lit a Major, picked up the phone and prepared himself for the gruff ribaldry.

Pete Nugent treats the phone the way he treats his bar staff – he bellowed down the line: "Kevin! Long time. How're they hanging?"

"Hairy as ever," said Kevin, laughing hysterically and then wincing at his own giddiness. He hoped Pete hadn't heard about his fall from grace – or the break-up with Linda.

"I hear you're on the wagon?"

"Yea, the barman's union held a crisis meeting."

"And Linda's done a runner?" Like all publicans, Pete just oozed compassion.

"Marriage isn't a word, it's a sentence," Kevin managed to shoot back, "And I've been pardoned."

"Alone again?"

"Naturally!"

He had almost managed to sound nonchalant.

Then Pete told him about the Gandon Lodge hotel; his dream for respectability after a lifetime running beer barns. Gandon Lodge was something Pete wanted to leave his two teenage daughters. They should have the things he never had, or wanted. So he poured his savings into sturdy concrete and fine mahogany.

"Something for the children," he said to Kevin, "You know yourself."

Kevin didn't know himself.

He couldn't allow himself to think about his boys now, except at night, in the morbid darkness of self-loathing. He had betrayed that dream. He was forced to apply for permission to visit them, in a house he once owned, where another man paid the bills. When he met his boys they had far-away looks and spoke in caged language, while Linda hovered. Tears would well up and he'd feel the craving to soak his memory in mind-numbing alcohol whenever he remembered how Jimmy, his youngest, used to shout at Linda. Angry and indignant Jimmy stood by his dad, the put-upon dad who was merrily guzzling away the family savings.

Kevin's pain was not from Linda's vindictive lies – or harder truths – but from the slow, sober memory of how his boys' unquestioning love faded first to suspicion and then to sullen anger. Soon even Jimmy greeted him with warm hugs and worried looks, while Linda taunted him with the memory of the day she piled the boys into a taxi as he stumbled helplessly down the garden path, anaesthetised to the pain and anger. When she saw her chance she first removed the boys, and then her wedding ring, the white circle on her finger announcing to the world: "Available – single, white female, with some baggage."

His boys were her baggage.

He knew he had blown it. And it was only the thought that he might still reach out to them that kept him terrified and on the wagon. The thoughts of her sharing their bed, their children and their secrets with another man hardly bothered him at all now.

"Gandon Lodge is the big dream," Pete had said softly down the phone, "I'm looking for someone to mind it for me, someone I can trust."

He put his trust in Kevin.

And Kevin knew that this was it. If he failed now, he would never climb out of the hole he would dig for himself.

When he stood up and dumped the empty Britvic box in the corner, the big tinker was staring at him again. "Are you all alone here?" he said.

It sounded innocent enough but Kevin answered cautiously: "Just me and a few workmen," he lied.

"And where did you spend the Christmas?"

"Here, alone with my demons." He laughed.

"Whiskey, whiskey everywhere and not a drop to drink."

"It's nice and quiet," said Kevin. "And the crowds will be back tomorrow."

"And children?"

"They live with their mother now."

The big man nodded and sipped his pint.

"Is Pete Nugent about?" he said suddenly.

Surprised, Kevin shook his head. How did he know Pete? What did he want with him?

The little man nudged into the conversation. "You seem to be all alone," he said. Kevin shot him a look and grabbed and lit a Major. But the big man scowled at his companion.

"Moxie's the name," he said to Kevin, "Moxie Doone." He smiled and reached out his hand. As he did, he accidentally displayed the top of the hatchet again, tucked away in its proxy holster.

Kevin tensed as he shook hands, realising he had opened Pete Nugent's door to an armed member of the notorious Doone clan. He heaped four spoons of Maxwell House into a cup, splashed boiling water on top and sipped the scalding coffee. The Doone family's feud with the Connor clan was legend in the west; they never met, except at funerals when old scores were fought over but never settled.

Pete had once told him of the legendary feud. "Everyone has a history, except for the Doones and the Connors," he said. "They don't have a history because all their past is present; they talk of their ancestors as though they're living down the road aways; old family war wounds are fresh-cut sores to them. They can't let it go."

That's what Pete had told him, and Pete knew travellers well. He had been a friend to the travellers. They were always served in his drinking dens. Kevin had once seen him sack a barman for refusing to let a travelling woman use the Ladies.

9

Peadar and Moxie soon settled back to their pints, Moxie telling stories of travellers who had been champions at sulky racing and bare-fist fighting; of those who had made names for themselves in England and America; and of the few who had given up the ways of their people. Kevin sat on a barstool he kept in the corner behind the bar and gazed through the panelled window. Rain bounced off the water barrels in the darkening courtyard. He fretted. If the rain eased, he could banish his two intruders, drive the water wagon to the nearest ditch, and then lock out the rest of the world again. But Moxie seemed too settled to move; and Peadar too volatile to move against. Then, Peadar picked up the coat he had thrown on a table, rummaged in the pockets and threw a mobile phone on the counter, as though it was a gauntlet.

"I wonder if Eamon and Seanie are about for a quick pint," he said to Moxie, with a sideways glance at Kevin, who got the message and rose from his corner.

"Right," said Kevin, as loud as he dared. He looked at his watch, as though he had some pressing business, something that needed his urgent attention within the four grey walls of the Gandon Lodge, on a cold and wet St Stephen's Day.

"It's time I was shifting you," he said.

Peadar turned red and sneered: "'Move along! Get along! Go! Move! Shift!' Is that the way it is?'

Kevin looked to the big man for support. So did Peadar. But Moxie's eyes were moist and distant. He was lost among his stories of ponies, caravans and jinny-joes.

Kevin turned to Peadar: "Two pints I told you, and that was it." He could feel the skin crawl across his chest, his body shudder and his leg muscles soften. But he held Peadar's angry stare.

Peadar's right cheek twitched. "We're not looking for trouble," he said, in a clinical, looking-for-trouble voice.

Quietly, Moxie stood and placed one hand on Peadar's shoulder, and stretched the other to Kevin's. Suddenly, he burst into song:
"My home the road
And no fixed abode
I must travel till I die."
He stopped and looked at Kevin. "Isn't Christmas a mournful time," he said. He shook both men, like a mother bear with her cubs.

"Have we time for a quick one?" he said.

Kevin shook his head.

"Just the two of us. And no more talk of calling anyone else. And then we're done."

"It's time I was locking up," said Kevin.

But the big man persisted: "Two pints. To bid farewell to this cursed time of year. No Christian heart could deny us that. We haven't slept since Christmas Eve."

Kevin knew he was in a dangerous corner. But he knew he would relent. He would give them two more, if only to let Peadar calm down, and to keep the big man sweet. Any man who had survived that two-day Christmas frenzy without sleep deserved some sympathy, he told himself. He had barely escaped it himself.

Christmas Eve and the world had been a drunk tank.

Frenzied partygoers accosted him in every shop and on every street. Loud, boisterous, giggling, weeping, consoling, staggering, jumping, slumping drunks of all ages bumped into him, muttered at him, chuckled at him, shouted at him and attempted to embrace him. 'The Holly and Ivy Crowd' he used to call them. Not used to drink, they guzzled freely, got sick and were sent home in taxis.

Kevin had fled to the tranquillity of the Gandon Lodge. He didn't care who was sleeping, he didn't care who was awake, he didn't care who was good or bad, for anyone's sake. Those who mattered were far away now, so he offered to play caretaker while the staff rushed to their own homes and parties, and Pete took his family to Paris for the two days.

All was calm and all was quiet.

He unplugged the television and worked all Christmas Day, emptying ashtrays and bins, carrying out bottles by the crate-load, stocking shelves, washing, sweeping, hoovering and sweating like a pig – the sweat of redemption. And when the day was done he retired alone to his purgatorial bedroom on the dusty third storey, with its long narrow hall, shaky wooden floorboards and dormer porthole windows peeking out over the darkened courtyard to the driveway beyond. He brought with him three turkey and cranberry sauce sandwiches, a pint of milk, racing forms for the next couple of days and sixty Major – twenty just for backup. It was a long way down from The Dorchester but a long way up from the morning infusions and four-hourly top-ups. It was the Christmas cure for his mangled soul.

Kevin watched the flurry of brown turn to black as he pulled two more pints. These would have to be the last.

"Have you children of your own?" he asked Moxie.

"They're with their mother too," said Moxie, laughing. He placed his strong hand on Kevin's shoulder and squeezed.

"Don't mind the whore," he said, "The world is filled with beautiful fillies just waiting to let you slip 'em the halter. And don't be rushed. Take it easy and slow. Easy and slow, that's the secret. But a man should have a family to go home to."

With that Peadar pulled himself up to lean over the bar, stared down into Kevin's startled eyes and said, "And remember, it's not the size of the nail, it's the hammer that drives it!"

The two companions howled at this.

"You're a bit of a hammer man yourself," Peadar said to Moxie.

"Your wife tells you everything."

Peadar froze but didn't respond.

"There we go then." said Kevin quickly, setting the pints under their noses.

"How do you know Pete Nugent?" he asked Moxie, to change the subject.

"How wouldn't I know my own cousin?"

"Pete?"

"Mind you, he's come a long way since we wandered the byways of England together. He fell out with the rest of us, gave up the ways of his people. Changed his name."

Kevin didn't know all he thought he knew about his boss.

"So Pete's a Doone?"

"The years don't change what's in your blood. We're up for a funeral. It's a very sad affair. All the Doones will be there."

A funeral. Kevin steadied himself. He tried to smile as his eyes hunted for the small jar of Maxwell House. It was nestling among the bottles of strong spirits that stood clustered together on a rickety glass shelf, delicately balanced.

Kevin had last come close to the Doones and Connors feud when he worked in hotel in Balsullivan. Both families thronged into the town from as far away as Southampton for the burial of one of the Doones. They brought with them their axes, their knives, their slash-hooks and their generations of bitterness. The row started when one of the Connors danced on a Doone grave. The next day one of the Connors was killed with a crossbow.

"A funeral?" asked Kevin, flicking on the kettle and pulling hard on the butt of his Major until it burned his lip, "A relative?"

"A man called Tommy Doone," said Moxie.

"King o' the Tinkers, unbeaten," announced Peadar, "The Doones will gather in their thousands to send him off."

"And we've come here to make our peace with Pete," said Moxie, "Let bygones be bygones. And tomorrow, after the funeral, why don't we bring some of the old gang back here to meet up with Pete. God knows you could do with the business – if only to keep your mind off that bad bitch."

Kevin felt cold sweat drench his back and chest but his mouth was dry and the rich aroma of the freshly pulled pints tempted him. He poured a Club Orange and Club Lemon into a pint tumbler and knocked it back; at least it would quench his thirst. The damned kettle was taking its time to boil.

He looked down the mahogany bar, at the mirrors, the glass shelving, the fragile chandeliers.

They'll wreck the place, he thought. And the reputation of the Gandon Lodge will be in ruins. Pete would never forgive him. And he would never work again. He felt the wash of alcohol come sweeping towards him, ready to lap him up. Willing him to submit. The battle was over. He could release the fragile grip he held on hopes for a new life. He could drown freely. It was beyond his control.

He looked up in a daze and Peadar was grinning at him. "And don't worry," he said, pocketing his mobile and grinning again, "There'll be no trouble." He almost chucked and said: "As long as nobody tells the Connors where we are."

Moxie's red face turned purple – and then he turned on Peadar.

"Say what you mean," he shouted. He grabbed Peadar by the lapels. "And nobody will tell the Connors where we are," he roared, pushing Peadar away from him, sending the pint flying. Peadar went tumbling back into a cluster of barstools. He stumbled back in indignation and leapt at Moxie. Punching wildly, he grabbed the big man's jacket – and then let out a terrifying yelp.

Whimpering, he held up a limp hand, like a puppy with a sore paw. And a scarf of blood swam across his palm and spread down his arm. Blood stains dropped onto Kevin's polished bar and turned into a river dripping on to his freshly shampooed carpet.

"Shite," shouted Moxie. He took the axe from his inside jacket pocket – the blade was smeared with blood – and he threw it on the same carpet. More blood oozed from the blade. Moxie reached out in sympathy to grab Peadar's hand and the little man yelped again.

Between blinding curses – most of them Kevin's – they managed to mop up Peadar's bloody palm, and bind the cut with the Gandon Lodge's cleanest dirty bar towel.

Eventually, the two settled at the bar again. Two more pints – medicinal this time – were obligatory. These would definitely be the last.

Kevin's head was in a spin. He pulled the pints without debate. He needed time to think. Tomorrow, the dining room would be full of chattering children showing off new toys to tired dads in brightly patterned knitted jumpers. They would be nice families, from nice homes with nice new toys. They were the families Pete Nugent had built his hotel for. It would not be the place to revive the Donnybrook Fair. Almost overcome by the scent of alcohol and defeat – a scent that had become all too familiar with him – Kevin felt an old anger growing in him; a raw outrage he had not known for a long, long time.

Fuck it, he said to himself. Fuck it, I'm not drowned yet. He would keep his fragile grip. He felt the ghost of the old days. Before he went bad. When pressure brought out the best of him.

Besides, he had a plan.

It was reckless and stupid. If there was anyone else around him he wouldn't tell them what it was, it was so laughable. But he was going to run with it.

The makings of the plan calmed him. And suddenly Kevin felt hungry. So hungry that he couldn't think. This was a good sign, he decided. He was back in control – or else he had lost it altogether.

Kevin decided that Peadar had joined the walking wounded and would be pliable as a poodle. And without his goading the big man could be trusted. He would leave them alone for five minutes.

He gulped back the coffee, made a mental note of the drink levels on the Paddy, Powers and Jameson bottles and galloped to the kitchen with the speed of a pony at the Laytown races, pausing only to wince at the darkening bloodstain on his carpet. In the kitchen he made up three lots of sandwiches with turkey, stuffing, tomatoes, onions, ham, lettuce and anything else he could find. He raced back. The bar was still intact. But the boys were meekly silent – and the Jameson was down a couple of notches. They had been clever enough to leave the Powers untouched. But what of it? It was Christmas and there was no damage done – yet. Besides, he had a plan.

All smiles, he handed up the lunch basket: "A bit of soakage, lads."

The three of them ate in silence. Peadar and Moxie – heads bowed and surprisingly subdued – gulped down their chunky sandwiches with slurps of stout, while Kevin inhaled deeply from his cigarette and swallowed each bite swirled around with the smoke and strong coffee, thinking about tomorrow.

"So, tell me," he said, making it sound like casual conversation, "What relation is Pete to the deceased."

"First cousin," said Moxie.

Then he lifted his head and addressed Kevin deliberately, almost formally. "There's not too many a settled person who'd treat men like us the way you have done," he said, choking a bit. Kevin warmed to him. He was glad he had trusted the big man; sure he was down a couple of whiskeys but he had known millionaires and lawyers doing worse when they thought his back was turned. And it had been a long time since anyone had a kind word to say about him; it had been a long time since he had given anyone reason to say a kind word about him.

Moxie leaned into Kevin's face; the strong smell of whiskey sullied the nobility of the moment, but Moxie reached into his jacket pocket, the one that hadn't carried a lethal weapon, took out a twenty-pound note and said: "Here, take for two large ones. We got a bit parched when you were away. I hope you don't mind. No offence intended." He bowed his head in mortification. Kevin didn't know if the shame was for swiping the whiskey, or the unwarranted display of honesty in front of a gobsmacked Peadar.

He took for the two large ones as Moxie clipped Peadar on the sleeve and buttoned up his denim jacked, showing a bulge over his right breast.

"We're gone," he said, "Thank you for your kindness, sir. We'll see you tomorrow. And don't be bothering with sandwiches." He winked and downed the dregs of his pint, "It's not grub we'll be up for."

As they left, the hailstones had turned to a drizzle and Moxie was singing again:

"For few men gave me camping space,

Aye and fewer called me friend…" he sang. Then he turned and grabbed Kevin by the hand, and burst into full flow.

"I came to Dublin city fair
In the year of fifty-nine
And I camped in Lansdowne's grim valley
With others of my kind
But Dublin Corporat-eeon,
Good Christians to a man,
Broke down our camp, uprooted us
Dragged out our caravans."

Kevin returned to his bar and sat alone in the splendour, drinking strong coffee and smoking. He hadn't felt like this in a long, long time.

At nine o'clock the next morning, the frost had cleared and a bright winter sun glared down on the gravel. Pete Nugent's Volvo S80 pulled into the courtyard and parked. He passed Kevin on his way down to the driveway, driving his water wagon. He waved to Pete as a church bell pealed through the cold air. He wondered if it was for the funeral mass of the late Tommy Doone, King of the Tinkers – unbeaten.

Kevin steadied the tractor. The two barrels were filled so high with water that it splashed over the sides every time he hit a rock. And he had hit a few rocks already. He had almost fallen off a couple of times and had to use one hand to hold on as he drove. But he held a tight grip and figured he'd got the hang of it by now. He looked back as two groomed and manicured teenage girls in Pepe jeans and Tommy Hilfiger T-shirts emerged from the Volvo. Pete had reached the front door, a look of bewilderment opening up on his face. Kevin turned back to his task.

Pete was staring at a funeral wreath made up from bits of tattered holly and ivy and held together with Sellotape. It was pinned to the front door. A note in neat but slightly shaky handwriting read: "As a mark of respect to the family of Tomas O'Duchain, a first cousin of the proprietor, who died recently, these premises will be closed all day Wednesday, December 27th. *Ar dheas lamh Dé go raibh a h-anam.*"

Work in Progress
Samantha McCaffrey

Sometimes big, often small
A slip of light in a darkened hall
The size of rain falling.

Full to the brim
With waves of words stretching fast
Scratching my waters.

Framed in tension, rods of steel
Holding up my sky.
No clear pool of sharp edges.
Frayed instead
By slashes of an unravelling storm.

A mire of ice and stones,
Rubbled limbs, smelting in embers.
This mesh of rash and bone
Set in cut glass.

Freg's
Cal Daly

Novelty always compromised my self-control. And it never seemed to matter what was new. I didn't distinguish between good and bad new. New is good. So when Cassie introduced me to the new fruit 'n' veg store round the corner from her place, I bought like I was opening my own store. It was called Freg's. I swear, you couldn't make it up. The guy's name was Fred. He came up with the name himself and he laughed a little harder every time he told me. I remember not being sure where he was from and thinking he was Puerto Rican. Turned out he was.

Anyway the strange thing was, the first time ever I went into his shop, like I said, I lost control and ended up literally spending more than I had. Of course I didn't realise this until I'd emptied a trolley full of his store on to his home-made counter. Cassie had no more cash on her so I ran next door to the ATM, but typically it was out of service. So I went back to make my apologies but he wasn't having any of it.

"Tiss no problem – is problem with bank only. All the time no working. This one beside never working. Other bank iss far away and I walk there and no working. I go krazy. No bank no problem."

Having shown no signs of recognising Cassie who was a relative regular by now, he nodded to me and said:

"No bank no problem. You come here all the time. Today you pay what you have and later or tomorrow you come again and you pay the rest. It's OK."

I didn't know what to do. On top of the obvious mortification, I now had to contend with being a fraud. Fred was giving me store credit on my first visit ever on the basis that I was one of his best customers. Finding myself in one of those situations where it was easier and I think for the best to leave the lie stand, I gratefully left with more fruit 'n' veg than I could eat and certainly more than I could carry, all the while fervently promising I'd be back soon as.

Barely out of my pjs and, if I'm honest, still in my slippers, I went back first thing the next morning.

"Why you rush? I know you, it's no problem. I see you all the time. It's OK."

I was reared to hold the door open for my elders and give them my seat on the bus. Smile and the world smiles with you. Say hello. Be courteous.

All that jazz. So when Fred the fruit 'n' veg guy was nice to me for no apparent reason I was nice back, no reason needed.

"So you live near by yes?"

"Yeah just a ten minute walk or so, by Hill's – you know it?"

"Yes yes I know. I drive by that way coming to here. There are four of you, yes?"

"Four of us?"

"Yes yes four of you friends that live together – the other girls I see them too, they come sometimes. But not all the time not like you."

"Yeah there's four of us – we've been friends since college so it's a good set-up."

The 'good set-up' line was my reflex response when people asked about my living situation. Why I felt the need to qualify my circumstances to Fred from Freg's I've never known. But he asked so why wouldn't I answer?

"And you all work close yes?"

"Yeah pretty much, that's what makes the location so good for us."

"The one in the pharmacy?"

"The pharmacy?

"Is that you in the pharmacy?"

"No that's not me, that's Rebecca in the pharmacy."

"Oh the bank? Is that you in the bank?"

Making no modest presumptions of my intelligence, I'd like to think it reasonable to assert I'm not stupid. Yet here I was, acting it. A strange man, apparently in every sense of the word, gives me first-time buyer's store credit and by means of gratitude I help him out with the remaining details he needs to be our fully fledged stalker. I was listening to myself giving up the state secrets with what felt like a surreal lack of caution. I caught myself supposing I'd feel really bad if he ended up kidnapping Rebecca from work, all because I'd freely told him anything he wanted to know, or rather, the few details he didn't already know. And yet I couldn't help myself, so on I went.

"No not me either, I work in an office close by but eh no, not in the bank".

"No not the bank. Then you would be no problem with paying!"

He laughed. He meant it.

I laughed. I faked it.

"Yes yes of course that is the red one in the bank yes yes you are in the office the brown one."

Had he not been eagerly tugging at his hair whilst distinguishing me, the brown one, from Liv, I presume, the red one, he might have lost me altogether.

Despite the significant part of me that wished he had, it seemed I wasn't done being amiable.

"Yeah that's it, that's Liv in the bank and me in the office around the corner."

I was actually excited for him when he got something right.

"Yeah that's it, that's Liv..."

What was I doing – we were probably going to end up as delicacies on his polystyrene shelves next week and it would all be because I thought being polite was sharing our details with the curious fruit 'n' veg guy.

I walked home reassuring myself that one of the girls must have discovered Freg's before me and been drawn into conversation with him just like I had. He seemed to know more than he could have guessed. When I mentioned it in passing over the next few weeks I was a little thrown to learn that of the four of us, only two of us frequented Fred's Freg's, and Kate hadn't been conversing with him. She actually commented on finding him strange, a little hot and cold even and she had neither warmed to him nor thawed him out.

Maybe he had confused us with another foursome and it just seemed like he knew more than he did. In his defence, I filled in most of his blanks. I couldn't blame him for asking questions when I was so forthcoming with the answers. Whatever the case, he didn't really bother me so I put it down to coincidental error and eventually forgot about it.

Though it clearly wasn't intentional, the first timer's credit had proved a great marketing ploy for Fred. Whether out of appreciation or guilt, I hadn't dared buy so much as a grape anywhere else since my first visit. The girls had switched to an apparently divine organic shop across the road but I was somewhere between stuck and sticking to Freg's. I was terrified Fred might spy me sneaking out of the competition so I never crossed into enemy territory. I felt bound to him and it didn't matter whether it was out of loyalty or obligation, Fred got my custom. I was cursed with the blessing of decency. It was a question of good manners. As were the chats.

"Try this new lemon tea. Let me know if you like."

I told him it was lovely – kinda fruity but with a kick. Obviously I didn't actually try it.

"Try these new blue berries – they're wild like your eyes. Let me know if you like." Sometimes I knew what Kate meant.

"So you like Hill's? Tiss weekhend we go there me and my friends. Last year the same thing we have a bar be que on this bank holiday weekhend and then we go to Hill's. You come it's no problem you bring your friends and you come."

I feigned disappointment brilliantly, explaining how my mother's birthday was that night and how it was so typical that there would be two things I wanted to go to. Doing the conga into Hill's that Saturday night I had long since forgotten Fred's invitation. Of all the places to pick how did we end up there? AND it was my idea! Not long after we'd taken straws to empty wine bottles did the realisation hit that we probably wanted more to drink.

"I know, lets go to Hill's," I said. "Genius," everyone agreed. Genius indeed.

Half an hour later, after making the ten minute journey to Hill's, I found myself heading up a train through the back. So devoted to being the engine I had long since lost touch with my carriages. It was only upon hearing an ominously familiar voice singing "it's no problem lets all do the conga ole ole it's OK" did I realise the girls had been replaced by the crew from Freg's.

"Your mother must be krazy – this party for her birthday is krazy."

I made Claire – two years my junior – pretend to be the birthday girl. She later hooked up with Fred's brother Marco and inadvertently earned my mother a reputation for being the 'kraziest mature lover' Marco had ever known.

"So we go to Hill's – me and Marco and you and your mother."

Claire dated Marco for four months and they never once commented on the fact that she looked notably younger than me and was ID'd twice in their company going into Hill's.

I was not dating Fred, though clearly he was dating me.

The girls said I was in denial, but it was still just a case of good manners for me. Grant it in this case manners a little above and beyond the call of duty. The novelty of both the fruit 'n' veg and the fruit 'n' veg guy had long since worn off. But I was in deep because of cursed courtesy. I was doing cash 'n' carry runs as dates and going to fruit markets every Sunday.

Only a few weeks into my regular custom I made a throwaway comment that I thought inaudible. I said jokingly that if he stocked tampons I wouldn't have to shop anywhere else. The next day he had tampons.

The cash 'n' carry runs became weekend trips. The Sunday fruit markets got further and further away so we started leaving on Saturday nights.

"Tiss very good hotel iss close to market so we go and make night of it yes? It's OK yes?"

"Its OK yes," I found myself saying, to everything.

"So we go to my home for the holidays its ok its good you meet my family and see my home. They will love you too."

"It's OK yes."

It would have been rude not to. I was taught to be kind and damn it, I was. I had been raised with a set of rules that I had somehow possibly taken too literally. I had somehow gone from giving up my seat to my elders to taking twice yearly holidays to Fred's parents.

Even the moving in thing was an accident born out of my inability to say no. When another drunken conga resulted in an unnamed resident (Kate) leaving the kitchen tap running, we all had to make other TEMPORARY arrangements. Because I didn't have the heart to refuse Fred's kind offer, I agreed to stay with him for the seven-to-ten working days it would take to dry out and re-carpet our house. Fred went to such lengths to make me comfortable. He even moved his herb garden outside, leaving the living room free for my 'girl' things "becoss here is only man things and that is no good becoss you are not a man".

See, it was tender and thoughtful moments like that, that saw me permanently staying temporarily over Freg's with Fred.

Three years later I wondered for how much longer and how rigidly I was going to adhere to these rules of etiquette I had embraced. I worried that I had taken a more serious approach to those rules than I might have liked or intended.

"So we get married yes? It's no problem yes?"

"It's OK," I said.

The Belfry

Anne O'Donoghue

I didn't really decide to stop talking, it just happened. It started as a game. I tried to work out how many words were unnecessary and I culled them. My sentences got shorter and more precise. The meaning was purified. And the responses were more direct. I began to see my words like the landing lights on an airport runway, their position and use essential in easing my access. They were necessary mainly to protect against hazard. And over time I could manage with fewer and finally with none. And the comfort of quiet was reassuring.

I sometimes missed making sound. Not for communal consumption, not as an offering or exchange, but only for itself. Then I would go very early to the café in the church courtyard in town.

Maybe it's the height of the ceiling or the sheer empty expanse of floor-space or the ordered placing of the odds and ends of bentwood chairs around un-peopled tables. Maybe it's the presence of the grand piano accompanied by a large plant, that dominates even this room. Maybe it's the thoroughly un-modern proportions, but something there is conducive to sound. The walls contain a stillness not generally available elsewhere. Sometimes it feels as if no one has opened or shut the door since 1850. Time like a shamed guest waits outside, too cowardly to cross the threshold and claim the space.

And there sometimes in a corner I will sit and tap my spoon on the side of the cup to shield a low murmur escaping from me.

Smiling
Ainín Ní Bhroin

"Have a seat."

He was at the top of the conference table, standing, when I walked into the room.

"Thank you," I said and sat down.

"I'm afraid Conleth is delayed in court and won't be joining us."

"That's fine," I said, emptying the contents of my bag onto the table. Then I looked at him for the first time. Jesus!

He looked up over his glasses at me. I got one of those oestrogen rushes that starts in your mid thighs and makes its way upwards – rapidly! Brown eyes. Long, black, spiky eyelashes.

Couldn't look at his eyes!

"I have been advised by the other side that they are going to put us to full proofs on this one. You know my particular view. And indeed a judge may not see the necessity of proceedings at all, in circumstances where a merely technical offence has occurred."

"I am *aware* of the possibility of that outcome," I said "but my client wants a full hearing *and* a conviction."

He leaned back in his chair and the fabric of his white shirt stretched across his chest. Oh Jesus I could see the hairs underneath – dark, jet-black and curly. Fuck! Come on. Come on. Deep breaths.

Can't look there either.

His hands. Hopefully he'll have horrible little chewed up nails and that would be the end of this. No! Square, functionally cut, not vainly manicured. There were even little bits, very very very small bits of loose cuticle skin. Strong, brown hands that moved slowly and deliberately as he spoke.

Not at this face, his chest, his hands. My eyes moved lower.

"Of course my instructions may change in the interim so I need leave to re-enter".

"I am with you on this... but he *is* insistent," I said.

Oh Jesus Christ! He crossed his legs so that his right ankle rested on his left knee. His crotch! My blouse was starting to stick to my back underneath my jacket.

I had to look up at his face. I could feel myself smiling, smiling. Smiling the way you do when you find someone attractive and you can't help yourself. I bit down hard on my lower lip, kind of on the left side. Stop it! Stop it! Concentrate!

" ... subject to the matter being withdrawn or prior to the adjourned hearing... "

He paused, took off his glasses, and looked straight at me for two hours. He put them back on and resumed speaking. I licked my lips and got a funny taste. I licked them again. What *is* that? I took a tissue out of my pocket and pressed it to my mouth. Then I looked at it. Blood! Oh fuck! Fuck! Fuck! Fuck!

I saw him in the Law Library on Tuesday and he winked at me.

A Tingle

Thomond Gill

Half an hour before the meeting
Still home (I live alone)
Spreadsheet eagled at my computer
Checking for mistakes
Running for another
Meeting in boardroom no. 3

The bus was late
A funeral passed.
This morning: dull, grey.
Not raining, not anything really.

I thought about the corpse,
Whether it smelled.
I thought of the Angel perfume
The kids wore to your funeral.
Too much, overpowering.

It had started when I got there,
smiled apologies:
Danish, coffee – tasteless.
Suits talked, mmm-d, argued.
Agenda item 15 – I'm up
standing in a stuffy room,
present, justify, answer.

Got back to my desk
e-mail, messages, file.
My boss congratulates me,
A pat on the back.
Then something else.
Cold. Life: dull, grey
It crept up. A tingle.

Not raining, not anything really.

Spoonful of Sugar

Eobhan O'Brien

Sleep last night crept the edges of the room
until finally a sleeping pill
dragged it in unwillingly.

Today I am red-eyed
uncooperative and snippy.
I drink my morning marshmallowed chocolate,
sweetness dipping the back of my throat.
It is only eleven a.m. and all I can think of
is bed.

It is only eleven a.m. and all I can think of
is bed.
And a cup of tea,
and a trashy magazine,
and Joe Duffy on the radio.

It is true I have been feeling under
the weather,
perhaps I need a tonic.
Or bed rest.
An afternoon would be enough.
I call a taxi.

I call a taxi.
Stop off on the way
to buy chocolate and
twenty euro's worth of celeb-tales,
the paper for substance.

By noon I am in my bed.
The wind and snow whooshing outside
the warmth of guilt inside my skin.

1970

John Edmondson

I did something today I never did before. You see, I know you. I've a great memory for faces – I see thousands of people here every year and a few stand out. Not just the Berties and celebrities but some ordinary people as well. I knew I knew you but I didn't know exactly who you were. I do now.

You sure didn't know me. And you still don't. I mean whoever notices grave diggers? Or whatever we're officially called now.

I'll never forget the first time I saw you. The three of you arrived in your old yellow mini. Like peas in a pod. All in your hot pants. Yours were red and plasticky. I mean Jesus you might've had a bit more cop on. You all fidgeted a bit, not quite sure what was going on or maybe even why you'd come. Well you certainly caused an impression even on a gorgeous day like that.

I know it was mid-summer because that night in Dempsey's the four of us were having a good laugh that we hadn't seen many arses that good. Then Joe put on a real serious face and said: "Well, I don't know. What about Lester Piggott?" We all cracked up thinking of Lester scorching down the race tracks with his bum high in the air showing them all the way home. Him and Nijinsky making us a little bit richer. And the World Cup had ended with us all blown away by the colour of Brazil with their goals and their short shorts. Brilliant green and gold time 1970 was. We called it the "Summer of the Bums". We swore we'd never forget you. Then Frances arrived and we changed the subject.

Great time but it didn't last.

The next time was a miserable bloody day in the early 80s. Remember them? Black days they were. Flags for Bobby Sands on the lampposts. The Stardust. Never making the World Cup or anything and Shergar getting nabbed. No fun at all. Joe and Pat had gone to England so the old crack wasn't there. Mick used to say the only good thing was that one of us grave diggers would be the last person left with a job.

Anyway, the three of you came, each with a fella. Professional looking. Nice cars. You looked very well – bit of style and this time you knew how to behave. I told the new lads about you afterwards but they looked at me as if I was too old for that kind of thing. Too old to laugh already? Jesus.

So I kept my mouth shut seven or eight years ago when you came again. Can't remember whose it was but you were in one of the first of the Mercs to pull up. Lots of them. Politicians and some property guys. Faces you saw in the papers. We did our bit and when we stepped back with the tapes you were pretty close. Very black and seriously stylish but strange. I didn't think anyone looked sad. I was disappointed in you. Life had gone, or changed, or something. Sorry, but that's how I felt.

I looked at the cards on the flowers afterwards. Oh yeah, fine words. Money makes a liar out of you, doesn't make you happy, I said to Frances that night. We had a good old laugh about the Summer of the Bums. Happy with ourselves we were.

Today was different. No sign of the other two bums this time and you were in the centre of it. The big cars were here again but you were really feeling it and looked like you were on your own. In our job, you get to know the different ways people take it and this was the real thing – no messing, not just shock or tears. It sounds strange but I was glad.

As I said, no one ever looks at us. We're just part of the machinery now, less respectful maybe than the old days, always told to watch the time and cost, get them in and out. So I think everyone was gobsmacked when instead of just stepping back I moved over to you, mucky overalls and everything, put out my hand and said: "Sorry." You looked at me for a moment, smiled, shook my hand and said: "Oh. Thanks. Thank you very much." Some guy moved over to you and that was it.

I don't know what came over me but I just know I went home feeling better about things.

And d'you know what? I think we have it all wrong. Every headstone in the place says when they were born and when they died. That's bollocks, means nothing. Instead why don't you say when you were really, really alive?

So, maybe I'll just have 1970 put on mine. What d'you think?

Haiku

Mary Flynn

Cornfields yellow and gold
Sacks replete, straw baled –
Frog slithers on stubble

New satchel, big lunch
Reluctant, handclasp tightening.
"No going home now!"

Early Friday hairdo –
Shampoo, cut, colour, highlight
"Pride must bear a pinch"

Just a Day

Kate Neil

Today I will ignore the dust on the mantel,
The dirty washing in the basket by the door.
I will hide the clocks, cover the mirrors.
Today I will tolerate no deadlines, no demands;
Be without sympathy.
I will wallow in anything I choose:
A good book, a bath, a memory, a dream.
I will pretend there are no beginnings, and no endings,
Just a day going on for as long as I need.
I will be deaf to the telephone, the doorbell, the guilt.
I will listen only to the birds.
I will have no doubts, no desires, no plans.
On this day I will be unafraid
To do nothing, to be nothing.

Dreamless

Nomleth Nyapokoto

Without a dream, he sat in despair.
He did everything and nothing came out of it.
Seemingly, he had no choice but to throw in the towel.

To give up was the obvious solution.
He was tired and depressed,
As he cuddled up with his head down to earth.

He was as caught up in sorrow
As a caged bird that wanted to fly away.
He felt smaller as it became darker
In the room…

The interior could tell all his emotions.
He seemed lonely as he
Cuddled up with his head down to earth.

He dreamt a dream without a vision.
A dream with no compass to lead him.
He was just an outcast banished.

He wept as he tried to figure out
What could possibly be the solution.
Had been a servant

Since the tenth Christmas of his life
And worked laboriously
For nearly fifty full calendars.

"I've seen my friends prosper
From being a servant
To highly respected positions"
He said grievously.

He mourned
As a woman who has lost her husband.
Hopeless he became
And dreamless he was.

Wallpaper
Clodagh Ní Ghallachoir

Houses were always her passion. She lived with her mother and father in a flat over their café. Margaret didn't like the fact that she had to let herself in via a side door and walk up a flight of stairs before she got to the door of their flat. She felt that there was something shameful about it. All of her friends lived in houses. Houses with front doors and gardens. Two-storey houses and bungalows.

When she walked home from school every day she made sure her route included particular streets which featured her favourite houses. It took longer to get home but to her it was a little piece of heaven. She liked to imagine what the houses were like inside, how many rooms they had and how they were furnished. She thought a lot too about the people living there and what their lives must be like. She wondered what it would be like to live in one of those regal redbrick houses with their sash windows and railed gardens. She always knew that her life would be very different if only she had a house. She could bring friends home with her and make noise without having to think about the customers down below. She could open the front door with a flourish and welcome people to her spacious dwelling. Best of all she could decorate the house and really make it her own.

When she was a teenager all of her friends kept scrapbooks. They spent hours poring over pictures of Bob Dylan and George Harrison. Carefully trimming the cuttings to fit the dimensions of the sugar-paper pages. For the sake of appearances Margaret half-heartedly dedicated a scrap-book to Mick and Marianne. She brought it out when she had to. She had another secret scrapbook, which she kept in an old suitcase under her bed.

For months her father had been complaining that his Reader's Digests were disappearing. He blamed his wife for being over-tidy. Years later he discovered a trove of hacked periodicals at the bottom of Margaret's wardrobe. She'd always been a strange child.

Creating that scrapbook was a labour of love. There were all kinds of pictures in it. Georgia Pacific tangerine oak flooring, Frigidaire twin refrigerator-freezers and bright red winged Knoll Associate armchairs. She luxuriated in its contents. In her mind's eye she could see her house. She knew exactly how she would furnish every room.

What she thought most about was the wallpaper. While her friends were obsessed with pop music and the latest fashions Margaret was consumed with op art. She had seen Bridget Riley's work in magazines and newspapers. She loved the solid blocks of black and white and the way they jarred as the patterns progressed. If she ever got a house that was what Margaret wanted more than anything. A room papered in bold monochrome stripes.

When she left school, like most of the girls in her class Margaret enrolled in a secretarial course. Her days were filled with double entry book-keeping and Gregg's shorthand. She wasn't the most outstanding student in the class but she was consistent and reliable. She got a start in the typing pool of a large firm of solicitors, Dolbey, Sullivan & Partners. Time passed as she transcribed Dictaphone tapes. She grew to enjoy the mental space the typing pool provided for her. In the evenings she went back to the flat and her scrapbook. Working meant that she could treat herself to magazines and this added a whole new dimension to her plans for her future home. Now there were pull-and-clean ovens and matching bed linen and towels, all with the Good Housekeeping seal. What she still wanted most for her future home was the black and white wallpaper in all its shaded splendour.

Margaret's dependable nature and her accuracy as a typist were recognised over time. A position became available as secretary to Mr Smyth, one of the partners at the firm. To Margaret he seemed to be an austere sort of man. He worked hard for his clients and he expected the same diligence from his secretary. To him she was Miss Brown. He grew to appreciate her silence and compliance. He wondered that she had not been poached by some of the more senior partners, given her abilities. As time went on he came to appreciate other favourable qualities in her, and then he came to see her in an entirely different light.

John Smyth had been close to his mother when she lived. Some would say too close. His father died when he was ten and he had become the head of the household and the undisputed centre of his mother's world. John knew what it was to return at the end of every day to an oasis of domestic order. Mother had impeccable taste and this was reflected in her home, which after John, was her pride and joy. He felt her absence most acutely when he ate alone, seated at the head of the vast mahogany dining room table. It was during one of these solitary evening meals that John had an epiphany. An image came to him of a similar table. The boardroom table in Dolbey Sullivans' to be precise. The table had been carefully and precisely laid in preparation for the weekly partners' meeting. Standing at the head of the table surveying the fruits of her work was Miss Brown. The parallel came to him in an instant. With the right advice she could be moulded. She would never replace Mother of course, but she could certainly be moulded.

It was a surprise to Margaret when, one Friday as she was leaving the office, Mr Smyth asked her if she would join him for dinner the following evening. For a long time she had to remind herself to call him John when they were not at work. Within three months he had asked her to marry him. It had been clear from the outset of their relationship that its foundations were practical more than anything else. John had lived a bachelor's life for many years now. He hoped that Margaret would restore the order and routine to his private life that she brought to his professional life. Margaret herself, though surprised at his proposal, readily agreed. She was never gone on the uncertainty of going to dances, wondering whether tonight would be the night that she would meet the man of her dreams. She knew that life with John would be safe and repetitive and she thought she could live with this. She would have to leave her position at the firm of course, but John had a large Victorian redbrick crying out for attention. For the first time in her life Margaret felt that she was within reach of her dream.

After a small wedding Margaret and John settled into their new life and schedule together. He left for work early and returned late. She was devoted in her mission to modernise the house. She endured his monotonous exertions in the bedroom. Lying limply on the nylon sheets she thought of Biba curtains.

Initially John gave her free rein. Gradually though, he began to resent the evenings when he returned home to find the bathroom decked out in garish Dacron curtains with coordinated towels. He missed the heavy dark drapes from the living room, which she had replaced with more psychedelic synthetics. He knew his mother must be turning in her grave. She had been a paragon of subtle décor, a virtuso of tasteful florals. His favourite armchair had been dumped at great expense in favour of a mock regency stratolounger. He gritted his teeth and bottled up his anger.

There came a time when Margaret had accessorised the house to her heart's content and she was ready for a bigger project. No amount of matching bed linens, curtains and towels could shift the concept of the room with the op art walls from her mind. This would be her space and she would take time there every day enjoying the realisation of her dream. Double doors connected the living room and dining room and these could be removed and a wall added. Since the new kitchen carpet had been laid it was nicer for them to eat in there anyway. John had reluctantly agreed to her plans for the conversion on the promise that the rest of the house would remain structurally unchanged.

Margaret thought her heart would burst with pride the day she returned to the house having purchased the wallpaper of her dreams. She waited until dinner was over and brought John into the half-finished room to unveil her beloved wallpaper. The black and white jarring stripes were the last straw for John. He had to put a stop to the destruction of his home.

Time passed and fashions changed. The sixties rolled into the seventies, which trundled into the eighties, then the minimalist nineties. The new millennium arrived. It was time to let the house go.

When the house came on the market most potential buyers found it difficult to see beyond the worn shag pile and the avocado bathroom with its dark marlite panelling. Miriam and Hugh saw the promise as soon as they walked into the house. They were looking for a home with conversion possibilities and to find something that had restoration written all over it in addition was too good to be true. Their offer was accepted within a week and Miriam began talking to their architect immediately. The vision that she and Hugh had was to restore the house to its Victorian splendour. The place would have to be gutted naturally. All of that awful sixties kitsch would have to go. On that subject Miriam had been wondering for a while if Hugh was losing the plot. The worst room of all was a migraine-inducing black and white cave at the back of the house. Hugh had seemed quite taken with it, making jokes about the jungle room. Well Graceland was not part of the grand design and he was soon reminded of the refurbishment of the dining room and how different the room would be with double doors leading through to the drawing room. If he wanted a den they could convert the attic eventually. Steam stripper in hand Miriam began the task of ridding the back room of its hideous wallpaper. The builders would be starting the next day and she could not wait to get more light into this space.

From their place inside the wall Margaret's bones shuddered as her dream of the ideal living space was torn and scraped from the walls around them. The wallpaper would be going and soon so would she.

Japan – Easter 1995.

Ainín Ní Bhroin

What I wouldn't give for a cheese sandwich now. Tempura and noodles morning, noon and night. The priest turned up for the show today with a gorgeous young Brazilian boy in tow. My mother had told his sister I was coming to Tokyo to see if he would offer to give me Japanese lessons.

Jenny had another breakdown last night and Clive rang my room to bring her up a couple of sleeping tablets. He was in bed when I went in and she was in a terrible state. She's running out of time, she said and Clive says no. It's all a bit of a crisis. I wonder she travelled so far to start this up and we have two shows tomorrow. Gave her the pills and went off with Hiro. Japanese men are small. I mean minute. When I reached down under the quilt it felt like I had a pencil in my hand.

Lots of British around because of the RSC thing. They are all really loud. "Super", "Yah" they say all of the time. You know when the waitress appears with the coffee pot in the morning they go "Ah" like it's some big surprise or something.

There is a threat of a terrorist attack tomorrow.

Another late night. Went back to Ella's room to drink vodka. Larry too. I'm hooked. I'm sure he likes me.

It was Easter Sunday. I wanted to go to visit this famous temple over at Yotsuya. But it was all a bit much really. Would have to find the Marunichi Line, buy a ticket, follow the map – which was in Japanese only etc. Totally traumatised me, my last attempt to travel alone.

Everyone is so servile. It's starting to get on my nerves. Bowing and looking humble.

Went to a traditional Japanese restaurant with Hiro. Had raw tuna and raw octopus with soya sauce and spicy green mustard. The octopus wouldn't go down my neck. It was ice-cold, lumpy and wouldn't break down in my mouth, as if it was not meant to be there. It tasted of perfume and smelt like ammonia. I was lucky I didn't vomit. The tuna was just as bad. You only smell it when it's in your mouth and you start to chew it. Went to see Kabuki in Ginza afterwards and then on to a German bar called The Ginza Lion. Larry wasn't in the hotel bar when I came back.

Bullet train to Osaka. It travelled so fast I couldn't see anything out of the window. Passed Mount Fuji but it was obscured by clouds.

Ella tells me that Larry will never have either a relationship or an affair with me. She seems very certain.

After Opening, which went well, we all went to Murphy's in Osaka. I wore my Issey Miyake scarf. When in Rome. Clive and Jenny came too. She broke down after a couple of glasses of saki and told everyone that Clive would not give her a baby. Onwards then to La Tropicana, a Latin American bar where I drank tequila cocktails and danced for a while. Needless to say Larry is a great dancer. He met this French woman called Grace who wrapped his dreadlocks around her wrists. I met Takahashi on the rebound. He was not a great dancer. He was not great at anything.

Larry had arranged to meet Grace the following night. We decided to tag along, me, Hiro, Mossie, Ella and a few others. We suspected she'd know places to go where you wouldn't have to pay consumption taxes. We waited with her in the hotel bar. But Larry wasn't answering his room phone. Ella went up to try to get him but she came back down without him. No joy. We went to a restaurant on the 28th floor of this building. It was swaying and like everywhere else the food was inedible. I drank about fifteen bottles of Chochu. After an hour or so Grace left. She said she was having trouble with her knees. Nothing the matter with her wrists though, was there? Everyone knew she was just dissapointed because Larry was a no-show.

Despite the fact that it was 4.15 a.m. when we got back I thought I'd look in on Larry. I knocked as loudly as I dared. He didn't answer. I went to bed on my own.

None of the musicians turned up on time for the music call next day. Susumu was like a bull. Ella went on the rampage. She dredged up everyone then except Larry. I think now it was probably Clive's idea to ask the head porter to check his room. "You go with him," he said. So I went.

The first thing I noticed was this substance like carbonara on the pillow. Carbonara made with fatty bacon because it was more white than pink and cream. I stood in the doorway. The porter disappeared. They've seen everything in Japanese hotel rooms. There's the one about the fat American with the twin teenage girls and the Alsatian. Larry was dead.

Ella told me afterwards that Larry'd had this big drug thing going for a few years. She thought that he'd quit apart from a nightly bit of draw. Although lately she'd been keeping an eye on him all the same, she said. Some eye.

"The show must go on," Clive said and we played to a full capacity 2,500 seat opera house that night. He sang "Honeysuckle Rose" especially for Larry. He wished him a long and happy life in Rastafarian paradise. This was a big gesture. Huge. Usually he brings a woman up from the audience and makes a big production out of giving her a red rose at the end of this song. That always goes down really well because Japanese women are very giggly and they take millions of photographs. Then they tell all their friends and before you know it you've a sell out tour.

And that was it. Japan – Easter 1995.

Fighting the Waves

Ellie Madden

On a dark night in November the muse hit. Drawn from my bed at 5 a.m., I donned the pea-green dressing gown and waited, fingers poised with PC purring in my own room, with time and solitude, and waited and waited and waited with all my systems in place. My time to write had come.

Sitting there I saw myself in the context of such greats as Jane Austen, writing meticulously dipping her quill by candlelight, or Virginia Woolf wearing knitted fingerless gloves bashing away in her lighthouse, or Sylvia Plath sitting up in bed on a night such as this. Overcome, I questioned my own greatness and wondered how I would find a rhythm to express all the form locked in the darkness of my brain cells. Fumbling, I now rejected every word that rose in my mind as too trite, too simple, too mundane. Nothing stirred except the odd scraping on the cobble lock as a leaf lifted in the breeze. Sitting there I longed to be immersed by the electrical sea of inspiration as my thoughts bobbed aimlessly over my life, dedicated as it was to accruing artistic experience. Dear friend don't you know yourself how I tried in my past? Haven't I immersed myself in folklore and fairy stories and tall tales? I have travelled the world in search of the great story. As I sat in my lovely room I pondered on days wandering over bogs and cycling on grey stone shores, or immersed up to my oxters in teeming lobster pools in search of elusive crustaceans or in swollen rivers looking for fish all in search of art, not to mention going up mountains in foul mist and peering into the great void for hawks. Still not inspired I have folded myself in fields of literature, awash with despair and longing for the perfect note. At various stages I have tried yoga, fighting, and writing while driving, and still the muse passed me by. Tonight I know she is with me as my fingers sit frozen on the keyboard while my eyes water with intensity. I am awash with excitement one minute only to be jettisoned to the depths of despair the next as the realisation of the newfound challenge bites.

Sitting here about to write my novel there is a feeling of exquisite isolation, and just for a fleeting second I am aware of her abstract presence as she alights on my right shoulder: a snow-like creature, her gossamer wings making music in my hair. It's my very own muse. I am possessed. My fingers relax. I float along, seeing me from her vantage point. The author is present. My books pile high in front of my glassy eyes. I am in a bookshop somewhere hot. The sun beams in. I can glimpse the sea as it shimmers in a summer haze. The books are all in a language I don't understand. All I recognise is my name on the cover. There is a long queue and people are jostling to get close and touch me. It's just a bit uncomfortable, so I move on. I am in bed drinking champagne and I can see all my friends out there, crazed with jealously. Gone is the cowering creature I once was, and so day one ends in a blaze of success with not one word on paper.

My head is full of books I think I will write and these are my psycho-babies. No one knows what's going on in the seclusion of my own room. I dress, go out and function on another level, do my shopping, collect the dry cleaning, do the ironing and nobody at all recognises my fame.

Day two and I now look forward to my date with the muse. I even light a fire in the room, turn out the light and add a couple of candles for atmosphere. I leave the curtains open so that the breast-feeding insomniac across from me can envy me as I purr with words. Today I relax into childhood explorations and lapse into a state of pyrotechnics, coming out of my daze of materials to hear the newspaper fall through the letterbox. By now my dreams litter the room from floor to ceiling (still not a word on paper). There is a great sense of happiness all around and I know the muse is there, dancing around all over the place in the flickering firelight.

By 10 a.m. I am totally detached when Madge my friend of twenty years from up the road appears outside my window. She is actually banging on the glass to get my attention. Somehow I rouse myself to answer the door. "Gosh I was so worried when I saw you sitting there with that look on your face with the fire on and all the candles," she gasps. "I kept ringing the doorbell but there was no answer and then I looked in the window and noticed you were there all the time. I'm sorry, but I don't understand what is happening," she says, invading my sacred space and sending the muse straight up the chimney. No dear reader you understand exactly how I feel. I could strangle her standing there as real as could be, criticising my room layout and destroying my atmosphere. "Look at you. Why are you undressed? Anyone could be looking in at you. Don't tell me you have been here all night. Have you been drinking?" she finally asks. Horrified, I manage to inform her I am writing a book and do not want to be disturbed. "Let me sit down for a minute," she says taking over my writing chair. "You writing a book. About what may I ask?" Because she is my best friend (or was up till this point) I say nothing yet. Suddenly I am aware of her panic.

We know so much about each other and from her point of view what I write will be very important. I know she is the kind of person who would be the first to scrutinise my work for any references to her in it. Well if that was all that worried her I am happy to live with it. Then suddenly and from nowhere I am suffused with a white-hot anger and I am screaming and raging against my very best friend who has shared my most intimate moments. I run at her and wave my hands, screaming obscenities all the while. All the pent-up anger of a lifetime spills over the head of Madge, who stands looking at me like a fish out of water, mouth open, gasping for air in the hot room. "God it's hot here," is all I hear her say as she backs out while I rail out against my parents, bosses, teachers, lovers and friends. "Honestly you are not yourself, I must go. Please give me a ring when you get better," she implores, all the while backing away from me at speed. At that moment I realise I don't want to kill her but I do want to be alone with myself. She's gone and not a word written. Still, I am having fun.

As the weeks progress I realise there must be some structure to my insane fantasies. In my saner moments I realise I am lapsing very far into unreality and decide to put a limit on my musings. I apologise to Madge and agree to go for a walk with her every evening and I pledge to give her a progress report on each day's work. We are friends again; as long as she understands that when I am in my room in front of the fire, candles lit and the curtains open, wearing the pea-green dressing gown she is not to disturb me, we will remain that way. I don't expect what happens later. As time goes on Madge begins stalking me by day and avoiding me at night. It's hard to describe how bizarre it all becomes and all because I express an interest in writing a book.

There are days when I lapse from reality so far that when the newspaper falls through the door I dash out and scan the property pages, as I now feel with the royalties from the novel I will be able to afford a place more suited to my delicate artistic sensibilities. A place in Dalkey or Dun Laoghaire right on the sea would be nice, preferably with electric gates and cameras so as to keep away busybodies like Madge. She keeps walking her dogs up and down by my window and often destroys a perfectly good fantasy with her carry-on. It's as though she wants to hunt away my muse with that awful mongrel of hers. My imagined wealth is now growing, and I am convinced the fame from my first book will catapult me into another stratosphere. These are days when I spend all my working hours counting my royalties. I really do need a good accountant. For the moment I will endure being stalked by that women and her infernal pest of a dog. There are days when I actually begin to plan a sequel. Still the written word eludes me.

There are times when it's a case of shop or starve. I dress, venture out into the real world, half expecting to be mobbed and have people rush at me with my book looking to have it signed, but all is calm. It's a pregnant pause I tell myself. I meet people I know and they act normal. People from the golf club invite me for coffee and we discuss politics and we discuss the winter league and arrange games during the week. At times I have to hold myself back and not tell them about my secret life as an author. Somehow I cling to the faint thread of reality that's strong enough to keep my mouth shut for now at any rate. I stare at my image in bookshop windows as I look for my beautiful work of art. It's not there yet. Sometimes I wonder if I am suffering from writer's block. Could it be like tennis elbow? There must be a cure, the equivalent of a massage for the mind.

Next day I am lashed to the keyboard, drawn by the invisible blood bond that has grown between us like we're shackled to one another. It's practically umbilical! Does the machine feel it too? Still I have written nothing, but have managed to explore many spacious rooms in my mind, travelled over centuries, held imaginary conversations with dead people, befriended famous artists from all ages and spotted the muse dangling from my chandelier, caught in a ray of sunlight when she thought I was only dreaming.

One day folds into the next in my phosphorescent haze. Sometimes I struggle for that elusive first sentence that's going to suck the reader into the plot, holding him there like a rabbit caught in a headlight. I tell myself it's the perfectionist in me that cause the block. Then the self doubts come charging in, maybe I should take lessons in stand-up comedy or dancing or white water rafting, flying, archery or learning French. Then I realise that would be simply silly, as I have no interest in any of these things. I am suddenly possessed by hatred. There is Madge (my primary enemy) with her awful Podge (I think I mentioned the stupid dog before. You should see her house. Her sofa... well suffice to say you, my dear friend, would avoid sitting on it at all costs. There are enough hairs on it to stuff cushions). Anyway I don't care if she refuses to open her door to me night or day. Of course she peers at me all the time. It's positively unnerving. My hatred embraces every successful person ever born, especially the dead writers who got there first. The room is rotating, the PC is practically on fire, the candles are gone out and I run around like a mad thing looking for the stupid muse which I now blame for all my woes. If it were doing its job the book would be finished by now. Instead she spends her time dancing on the end of the flame or abseiling down the drops of my light fitting. I know she is rolled up in a ball somewhere and is avoiding me. Another day wasted. I treat myself to a cup of mint tea.

Today I get up earlier and light the fire, start on a new set of candles (these are fancy and have lots of glitter as they are part of the Christmas selection). Time is passing. I turn on the PC and dream of the famous friends I will make now I have become famous and how I will spend a lot of time in planes where I will watch people read my book. I will stop people in the street and say "do you know I wrote that?" Immediately they will want to bring me home and introduce their friends and make me a dinner guest where I will be the most interesting creature in the room. All day long I dream, I forget to cook dinner. I am under pressure to meet deadlines. My agent, the muse and Madge are putting me under the microscope. I begin to see it's not easy being an artist, known or unknown. I have a brief bout of anxiety and think maybe I should take up acting. At least I could stay in bed in the mornings and stay up late and drink lots of champagne and have opening nights and end-of-run parties with really beautiful people instead of filing my nails endlessly as I really do, at five in the morning. Still not started.

Now the candles are hissing and spitting and the firewood must be fresh because it wheezes and sparks as it burns. The candle grease has spilled onto my writing desk and the furniture is covered in mountains of ash. It's like Vesuvius with all the hissing and sputtering. I am beginning to think the chimney needs cleaning. We really don't need a chimney fire coming up to Christmas. All in all I am tempted to abandon the artistic life. I should have been a nun. Then, maybe thinking of the contemplative life calms me down, and I am transported to find myself nominated for the Orange Prize. I spend ages over how I would receive the good news. Would I get a letter in the post? Would it be one of those modern see-throughs like one often receives with invitations to prestigious events, or would it be just plain white and ordinary looking? Could it possibly announce "nominee for Orange Prize" somewhere on the outside? (My postman would be so impressed and he would definitely tell Madge because she always discusses what passes through every letterbox with him. I told you I know her well.) I see myself turning it over in my hand.

Normally I just rip open my post as it mainly contains just bills and promotional stuff. Then maybe I would read it in the newspaper. I could see the bold headline: "First time Irish author nominated for the Orange Prize," or I could hear it in the news. All this presents no fear in my soul, I can cope with winning.

Fuelled by my success, the next day I am back dreaming of great reviews by artists who up till now I would have admired from a great distance. They would say things like "great new voice," "page turner," "hilarious," "bought it on holidays and read it in a day." What accolades. Small wonder I was chosen for the Orange Prize, not to mention the reception it got on The Richard and Judy Show. Up to this moment my greatest worry was the sequel. How would I every live up to my first novel? Everyone would want me. My publisher would be looking for more. Newspapers and radio would vie with magazines for live interviews. Finding time to write would be difficult.

I wake up to a new day feeling as free as a bird left to build its nest in the reeds of a fast flowing river. Inside my head feels swollen from all the thoughts swilling around. I know there is nothing to inhibit my artistry except myself. In the darkness of my mind my psycho-babies run around crashing into one another.

I work frenetically then wake up one day. It's Christmas Eve and I find myself in Brown Thomas the sale has burst into full swing and the poor irate exhausted shop assistants are ready to drop and enter the author with no Christmas presents bought expecting to find everything in the correct size and at rock bottom price it's impossible to make one's way through the mingling half-drunk crowd of revellers all like me trying to buy pressies for loved ones and Madge who finished wrapping the perfect gifts way back in October I grasp at a tie from the huge rack of ties and immediately bring down a cascade of silk that spills all over the counter and onto the floor at this point it is important to note that I have been working hard all morning and am not afflicted by drink and am merely in a hurry and furthermore I was shoved by that drunk who bumped into me small wonder the poor shop assistant throws her eyes to heaven as she takes my credit card and feeds it into the till then there's the small question of the PIN which I have forgotten so long had it been since I used the stupid card I move on and leave that exhausted assistant to sort her ties and caress her calf with her other foot throbbing with pain just dying to go home and put feet up with a glass of wine in her hand but there's

Santa Claus to be organised for the children and god knows the turkey to be stuffed and god knows will I ever get to bed thoughts going through her head while I join the queue for Jo Malone and buy nine bottles of the same perfume for all my sisters daughter mother cousins and have it all wrapped there and then of course the stupid perfume is not in the sale and I am now laden with bags and I dash to linens to find the sheets I promised to get my mother months ago now are sold out totally I am in a quandary and decide to text her and meanwhile I am being shoved and ignored by another assistant who is toppling under a mountain of towels some silly man with a top hat and tails is buying and threatening to bring me down with her honestly the things you see in town on Christmas Eve are unbelievable. Finally I make my way out of the store now carrying four half-price handbags two pairs of Marc Jacob shoes one for me the other for the mother to make up for the stupid sheets nine bottles of perfume (I forgot mother had also been included in the perfume not reduced binge; at least one person will be happy with her gifts I think forgetting about the nark she will be in all over Christmas over the stupid sheets) three men's sweaters husband and sons and who have I forgotten its just five to six and the tills are being checked and I bump into you of all people…!

Exhausted by all my pre-and post-Christmas exertions I revert to my old carefree life and spend my days pottering and shopping and going to the golf club and not playing because of the rain or snow or whatever. Most of the time we sit and drink coffee and talk to one another. Madge and I revive our friendship over a Christmas tipple and we end up hugging and kissing and making stupid promises to love one another forever. I even tell her of my feelings for Podge which might have been a mistake in retrospect. Now mind you she does mention the fact my room looked like an altar and she makes some disparaging remarks about my abilities to write.

The muse disappears, as do the early morning fires and candles. My room is the focal point of family festivities, which might be partially responsible for the loss of interest.

It's early February when I steal down in the middle of the night clutching my green robe around me, again possessed with the need to communicate with nature. It's uncanny. Darkness gives way to light. To be in my room and breathe is joy. Soaking the atmosphere is overpowering. While the damp is grey, all around are daffodils. The rain pours from the sky. Once again reality recedes. The tide is out and I am tsunamied into an isolated rocky shore somewhere off the west of Ireland. I am suffused with light pouring in through the big windows of my very own lighthouse that gleams in the sun. Outside the umbrellas are folded. Summer is still far off. Down by lapping waves the Brent geese feed. Eight have rested the night by the rocks. They come back every year. This is their feeding ground. A wild otter gazes longingly at the feast so close. They squawk and call, unaware of his presence. Close by on the rocks a young family, mum, dad, a little girl. She is all in pink. The man is on his hunkers. His camera is trained on the geese. The mother holds the child back with ease.

Spring is my time when childlike my eyes search for the hint of the first crocus a gentle growth the opening of a single flower then the next day and the days following there is a rush of opening petals and that hanging snowdrop gazes at me from the base of a tree or in a stranger's garden or in a big field and I am transfixed with wanting I know not what just a tug at my senses an awareness of the silent moves that change the face of the countryside from bleak and wintry one day trees bare branched mountains grey or even coated in an icing of snow powder the dregs of winter hanging on and on then next day it's all there the first signs of the gorse spring to life an overnight lightening bloom promising to fill the hills and cloak the world in its profusion like a sunburst through the dark cloud of winter and still it goes on the forbidden hidden world of growth and regeneration and buds everywhere shooting and sprouting and growing day by day and its all happening and I am sad and happy all at once wanting to touch the growth wanting to grow and stretch into soft shoots and immerse myself in the wave washing quietly over the land an unstoppable nature wave reborn each year with the arrival of the first birds of spring and the departure of the winter birds from trees and shoreline and the long days lengthening imperceptibly like the passing through of time and the ravages of age and the brightness of youth and promise and the resurrection of Christ at just the right time and chocolate and Easter eggs and socks and short sleeves and summer around the corner and the end of open fires and the mowing and the smells of the first grass of the season moving into the sea and the valley calling birds to make nests and set up home and lay fertile eggs and piloting salmon home in genetic leaps through vast tumbling seas and rushing waterfalls to its river of birth to find soul mates and continue on that tenuous cycle and the scents given out by the silent shoots filling all the air with a pollen bouquet and I sit by my fire and dream of summer, readers, reality and you.

all
good things
begin

in love

Listening to the Car Radio

Helena Nolan

Some songs are cousins
Others brothers
The same genetic cocktail
Shaken or stirred
There is not an ounce of
Shared material between us
And yet I am certain
We are the same tune.

You open your mouth
And I place the words in it
Rolling them gently
With my tongue
I lay my hand over yours
As you change the gears
My palm melting
Into the back of your hand.

My fingertips reach
Only to your knuckles
So I know
If the detectives come
One day
To dust for fingerprints
They will find
Only one set here.

At some point
You must stop the car
And open the door
I will lift my hand
From yours
Flesh shucked off the bone
Our sweat the only evidence

And that is easily rinsed.

For now our knuckles merge
In a double helix
Who knows where the bond begins?
Improbability matched
Only by beauty
Discovery by mystique
The answer that brought its own question
Like a fossilised shell.

But once you spent all day
With my trace on your hands
In that moment
We were the same scent
Impossible to capture
In a net of air.
You go on changing gears
And the radio sings.

The Everything Bagel

Eileen Kavanagh

I hurry to meet you. I feel guilty the way I treasure having you all to myself without all the interruptions of our real lives: husbands, children, work, elderly parents, houses, and graduate school.

Sharing this time together, it makes me feel young and powerful, like when all that mattered was you, me, Susie, Marianne, a six-pack, and Springsteen blaring on the transistor.

I spy you before you see me. You are sitting in the chair by the window with the golden haze of summer streaming in giving you an ethereal quality. I giggle inwardly thinking you always did have the face of an angel but the mouth of a longshoreman! Your bandanna pisses me off and your IV hovers like a ghost.

I kick off my heels and climb into your yet unused bed, fiddling with the settings. You wince. Hey, Doyleface, hit the call button and ask if they've got something for smelly feet. Medical science can cure most things today. Your words hang between us. I get teary-eyed and start digging into my briefcase. I plop the wax bakery bag on the bed stand. Its got two dinosaur cookies for your boys and John's "Everything Bagel": sesame, poppy, garlic, raisins – all the toppings.

Once when John and I weren't trying to be brave I asked him what he needed. He choked out "everything, just like before". Now the only solace I can offer him is a bagel.

£50
Ainín Ní Bhroin

Angela says the West Indian guys are very smooth, very sweet talking. What about me £50 though? No point in looking at the answering machine. 'Course he hasn't rung. If Karen gives me the Mercury cheque I'll go in to the bank on Friday morning to lodge it and he'll be there.

Met him at Arsenal at 7.45. We got a Chinese and went back to his flat. He reads these horror books and read me about six pages of this gruesome "Green Man" story. He loves it. I don't care what he reads as long as he reads to me. He's a pretty good reader although he mispronounced several words including *viscera*. He drove me home saying that he didn't want me on the trains on my own at night.He didn't kiss me. Just a peck because he said he had mouth ulcers. I ask him if he will pick me up at the airport next Sunday. He says "Yeah. Sure."

Went to Stratford East for a meeting with the stage manager re- props. He's as odd as ever. Seems I'm to do "bits of furniture too". Find it, upholster it, paint it etc. I ask you.

The skin on his penis was silky and very shiny.

Going home for a week. Called in to the branch and had a great long chat with him. About an hour in his bay. Arranged to ring him later with flight time. He'd be working at The Blue Note Jazz Club from 11.30 p.m. 'til 5 a.m. Rang his number about eight hundred times. Voicemail.

He didn't put his hand in his pocket once over three dates. One: I bought lunch in Bella Pasta up West. Two: I cooked dinner. Three: I paid for the Chinese and the wine. Not to mention the loan of the £50. I'd already booked my flight to come back on the *Sunday* of a Bank Holiday weekend, thinking I would be spending the Monday with him. He said he'd repay me on the 20th May, when he got paid.

Have to prepare for the production meeting on Tuesday. Have a head cold. How am I going to call him about me £50? If it was £20 instead of

£50. Two weeks to go before the show opens. Problems with the moon box. Bought a black chiffon dress in Jigsaw, High Street Ken. for Opening Night. When the run finishes I will be back in Tesco's to pay for it.

Called into the branch. He wrote me a cheque for £50. That's that.

Five days later got a note from the bank telling me that the cheque for £50 drawn against Andrew Lewis had been stopped. Angela pressed me to speak to his manager, Wayne Milby. She came with me. Andrew wasn't there. Had rung in sick. I didn't feel a hundred per cent about it. I was angry but I was scared at the same time. Mr Milby was pushing me to make a formal complaint so he could initiate disciplinary proceedings. Must have had his own agenda there. All I wanted was me £50. I couldn't ask Andrew myself to lift the stop on the cheque or to give me cash, because he wasn't answering his phone. Angela told Wayne Milby that I could no longer have a relationship of trust with a bank where an employee was allowed to use his position there to his own advantage. Dishonesty. Mr Milby would arrange for the immediate payment of £50 into my account. He apologised.

Then Andrew called me today. He just kept saying "Hello, Hello," in the nastiest little voice you ever heard. He hung up when I asked who it was. He knows what's happened. Told Seán, Lucy and Kweku his name and address and everything. Just in case. Must look for my Suzy Lamplugh personal alarm.

Not Mine

Eobhan O'Brien

Ours is the sound of a cracked bell
a knife scraping a plate
a much loved sat-upon CD
a shrill alarm on a hungover ear
a bin tipped by a marauding cat.

Ours is the sight of the last bus
leaving the stop
the red bill beside the eviction notice
the accusing pointer
on the weighing scale
the lukewarm hot chocolate
on a cold winter day.

Ours is the mesh of fork with fork
a badly cut toenail against neighbouring skin
a tongue on the metal of a pencil-parer
a woolly glove taken off with my teeth.

This is it,
nothing more.
This is it.

The Promise

Conor Ferguson

Autumn came blustering in, and there I was hurrying my way out to work one morning, my head all sore and your mother's pointy, tired words following behind me: "Grow up!" I think she said. The wind hooted and whirled and sent leaves scurrying about like children in a schoolyard.

The bus wouldn't be on time. I knew that. So I stopped to pick up a few conkers along the road. Conkers don't have it easy. They live the first bit of their lives all cosy and protected in thick spiky shells, with not a care in the world. Until they grow bigger and heavier and the autumn winds come and shake them to the ground. Their shells crack open and they pop out as seeds, born to grow into great big horse chestnut trees. But more likely to be squashed by cars, or bashed at the hands of small boys by other conkers on the end of some string.

In Paris, where I'm going to bring you one day, their French brothers and sisters – called chestnuts – are roasted on hot orange coals and wrapped up in paper cones for lovers, and children, to eat in the cold, with big puffs of steam coming out of their mouths. So you see, it's not easy being a conker.

Anyway, I picked up one of these conkers that was lying there waiting to be squashed or bashed or made into a tree. It was big and shiny, with one side all flat from the way it was lying in its shell. I held it in my hand: soft and cool and brown like a pony. I made a wish. Some silly thing. Then I hurried along, wondering what the day might bring.

What it brought was another missed bus, another ticking off from the boss, and news of you. Your mother's voice trembled when she told me, and she smiled in a way I'd nearly forgotten. Then we hugged – the three of us – for a long, long time. Not that you'd remember. You weren't You yet – you were just a tiny blob of life waiting to happen.

The news took some time to sink in, I don't mind telling you. Well, I do, but you might as well know it anyway. I felt a bit funny about the whole thing, actually. Why? I don't know. I thought there were all sorts of other things I wanted to do first. All sorts of things. Give up my job, that's for sure. They wouldn't miss me, but I wouldn't miss them either. Not when I was lying flat on my back on a beach in Thailand, or leaping out of an aeroplane in Argentina, or sitting outside a brasserie in Paris, writing some great book or other. I had plans, you see, I was going to go places, do things. But I didn't. Instead, I stuck around, waiting for you.

But, you know, when I look back now, I can't think why any of that had seemed so important. It wasn't that I didn't want you. It definitely wasn't that. Or maybe it was a bit. I don't know. We're only here for a short time, so we might as well make it a good time, as someone once said to me. I think she was Australian. But there was truth in it nonetheless. All those ancient cities waiting to be got lost in. All those wide open spaces and great deep oceans to be crossed. The smells, the sounds, the music, the colours, the feel of all of it. Out there. Somewhere else.

It always seemed to me that people don't ask to be born. They don't sign up for the embarrassments and the bruisings, the missed buses, the broken hearts, the disappointments, and the grief that are part of being alive. It's stuff that parents inflict on them. (At some stage this might make sense to you. When you're a teenager, say. But to tell you the truth, it's rubbish.)

The main thing is, sometimes people don't know what they want. They're silly really, people. But your mother knew – she wanted you. So we tried harder to be in love, because when you arrived everything would be good again.

We didn't tell anyone about you. You're not supposed to, in case something happens. It was our little secret, and that made us feel closer. But things were tricky. When you have a house, life becomes more serious. Houses are very pricey, so if you're not a proper grown-up when you buy one, you soon will be. You have to work hard and not be messing about with your friends. You have to... what was it she used to say? ...knuckle down.

Anyway, I knuckled down. I closed my mind to the panic attacks of: would I ever get to watch the sun rise again (without the accompaniment of your lungs shaking the walls)? Would I get to just bump into old friends and end up spending a mischievous afternoon roaring laughing in a pub? Would I be able to watch the TV programmes that I want to watch, or would I always be wondering how much of it you're taking in? Would there ever be such a thing again as wandering aimlessly around town, or going to the cinema for a bit of, I don't know, idle distraction?

And would I really be expected to spend my days making goo-goo noises and my nights reading the same nonsensical stories over and over and over again? And all those "but why, Daddies?" Would I be up to all of that? Would I manage? Or would I buckle and run?

That was the worst of it – the fear. So, I ignored all that. I looked on the bright side. I thought about the good things. I thought about you. I thought about the laughs we'd have. The stories I'd make up, and the way I'd explain things to you, and watch your imagination grow much bigger than my own. "What are the stars, Daddy?" "The stars are all the babies that will ever be. They are all up there, waiting for their turn to be born."

And I decided we'd all go on holiday. You wouldn't be able to see anything of course – by that time you were a thing roughly the size of… a conker, actually – but it would make everyone more relaxed, and give us things to talk about. Ten weeks had passed since our little magic chemistry had clicked and fizzled and done its work to make you. (Don't expect me to explain here. It's complicated.) We hadn't had much of a chance to talk about things – such as where to go, only somewhere cheap. Turkey. Estonia. Portugal. Morocco. Lengthy debates were had – good-natured, for the most part – and in the end, for some reason, we settled on Wales, which is not really anywhere that people go really. Maybe that's why I liked the idea – it would be just us again.

So, one morning in December, feeling sleepy and excited, we drove the car onto the boat and the boat took us to a place called Holyhead. Now, Holyhead may sound a little bit like Hollywood on the telly, but actually it's the exact opposite. In fact, all of Wales turned out to be a bit gloomy, so we headed into England. We spent a night in Chester, which is a very old-fashioned-looking place full of girls in short skirts. We had cream tea in a very posh hotel (your mother's choice) and a man in a cardigan told us, between bad jokes, that we should go to the Peak District. So we did.

We could see why it was called the Peak District, because it was high up. There, birds chattered on telephone wires and roundy hills said hello, as our little red car bounced along. The sheep said "Bah!" about nothing in particular – just cold, I suppose. It was just before Christmas, and everything was frosty and waiting. The sky seemed to be in a bad mood because the sun was going home; and evil, bony trees gave us the fingers as we vroomed by, but we didn't care. We had no plan. Just to follow our cold, red noses until we found somewhere cosy to stay. This was freedom.

Freedom is a thing you have lots of when you are small, but you don't really know about it until much, much later. So I hope you'll make the most of yours – no matter what anyone (like me, for instance) tells you.

We hadn't felt this free for a long time, your mother and I. We had been working very hard, for very long. Not that we fought all the time – but, yes, some of the time. And sometimes it was just very, very quiet.

Only, all that had changed when you came along. Well, the hint of you. The promise.

Bouncing along on the road, I think we both thought about that a lot, between the laughter and remembering all those adventures we had shared down through the years. We stopped at a little country churchyard. Rooks hopping from gravestone to gravestone, as if they were in some old black and white horror film and a big, spiky spire poking up at the heavens, in case God might forget about it.

Inside the little church, the smell of candles and the warbling of Christmas carols sweetened the air and warmed every corner, as the wind whistled and jeered outside. We sat into a pew and held hands. No need to say anything; just to feel our hearts slowing down, and be ourselves again.

Eventually we came to a small country town made out of grey stone. It was full of stern, no-nonsense buildings pretending not to shiver in the cold. But we could smell the ice forming in the air. We were very hungry. Nobody was talking. The wind was like knives, and then your mother felt something change.

The next bit either took forever, or happened very quickly. First we skedaddled to a chemist where teenage girls were looking at perfume and a man was blowing his nose like an elephant. The woman with bad hearing behind the counter eventually stopped smiling and gave me the directions to a tiny hospital, just outside town. The nurses were kind and spoke very softly. They said it was probably nothing to worry about. But they looked a little worried themselves.

We were put in a room with a special machine and I remember telling you to stay with us. Then I leaned forward to see a picture of you, but you weren't there. Just fuzzy rays; nobody home. As if the future had drained out of us. It was winter and spring felt very far away.

Now it is another winter. The night skies are clear and huge and peppered with endless tiny pin-pricks of light. The stars. I look to them and wonder can you see me?

Alan & Emma

Conn Redmond

Two childhood friends, Alan carried Emma's school bag – she'd filled it that morning with books, her lunch and a bottle of the ever present water she carried. The schoolbag seemed part of her and that made him feel happy. He'd hold it close and when she'd look at him, he'd smile and say what a nice day it was. Emma would laugh through the misty rain and say, "Alan, you're different, that's for sure."

He'd walk slowly to make the journey longer but Emma would skip ahead and taunt neighbourhood cats or pretend growl at the nasty dog behind the gate with the warning. Mr Blue would bang his kitchen window and mime insults for teasing his mangy dog, Emma jumping up and down at the gate, waving and shouting, "good morning Mr Blue," his face turning crimson behind the window pane.

"That was fun."

"Yeah," but inside Alan was glad to get away from the gate before Mr Blue came out, shouting he would tell their parents. If his mother found out, she'd skelp him with the slip of willow she kept beside the hall door, just for him.

She hadn't been well and when her money came through at the start of each month it was always worse, she'd be even more unwell, bottles emptied and she'd glare at Alan and shout, "you're a cut off your bastard father" and he didn't understand as he shook in the chair to one side of the fireplace. "The cut of him!"

Sometimes she fell asleep after all the shouting, or start crying and hug Alan and tell him how much she loved him. The horrible smell from her breath a betrayal.

Emma would pinch Alan's arm outside the school. "Alan, you can let go of the bag now, we're here."

He'd wait outside when classes were over. She'd bounce past with her friends and they'd sing "Emma and Alan sat under a tree, Emma touched his lovely knee and Alan wanted to take a pee," and they'd laugh.

But she'd look over at him.

And sometimes he'd walk on slowly alone but when her friends had gone she'd jump up behind him and say "surprise!"

"You don't have to take my bag," she'd say. But he always took it and felt better then. Just the two of them walking. And she'd say, in a sing song voice, "you're such a gentleman."

Mr Blue often stood watching for them at his gate and say, "just you wait," and Emma would laugh and blow kisses.

He'd look at her and murmur. "Hussy, that's what you are, a hussy." But he'd continue to look at Alan. "I know your Mother," he said one day. "You're just the same as her, a no good for nothing".

Emma asked what that meant and Alan said, "don't mind him, he's mad."

"He's mad alright," and she looked at Alan for a smile but he walked ahead.

The next day, instead of going home they went to the hill overlooking the village and sat on the grass under an apple blossom. Emma said they should never be apart; the world was full of mad people.

"Will you marry me, Mr Alan?" she said. Alan said yes, he could think of no other girl he'd ever want to marry, ever.

Wrapping their arms around each others' tiny waists, they hardly knew what they were saying, yet they knew exactly what they were saying. Somewhere they knew.

Skimming Pebbles

Maresa Sheehan

Skim One: a glancing kiss on the cheek
Skim Two: a smack on the lips
Skim Three: dips below the surface
And falls to the deeps

Magi

Yvonne Cullen

       We were useless
in the lives left to us that first spring…
Couldn't pass the days or sleep
or stomach our handlers' shimmying.
Dawns till the stones were warm
in petty kingdoms,
we couldn't have said for what
we stood and listened.

It wasn't that we'd been convinced
By what we found.
A poor child under a new star; every
new child's light as good as starlight:
that's all it meant,
and we went back
another way.

It was on the journey back
joy crept up in us: coincidence or caused. Till
well water was holy;
and the man who carried his wife along her last days;
a girl turning a corner in a town. The scent
of her wet hair.
We came home chalices.
And thrown from power
before we could divide it
nearer peace in the villages, we
died eventually:
isn't this what you'll hear?

Could you believe
the power whose puppets we are
opened our eyes again?
To a scrape of moon, tucked roofs…

My face: cold,
the others' dear faces;
in the dirt by the road
that red handle-less jug: thrown – aside
maker's mark of it
as the same broken world.

Since that night
how many journeys we've made
to uselessly have seen:
when dead are piled, the
questions gentle from their hands; and
we are used to it.

We wake already on our way.
By camel – the road a silk ribbon.
Or some years in
the only car
on a highway over yellow mountains.

Early villages send dogs.
Template jeans flag your balconies.
Laughter lifts sometimes
from men and women homebound.
In storms we wait out
they blow like
weed on strands; that laughter
polishes the stars, makes us remember being
celebrants a first time,
then we arrive
to one hut or one brick-field,
one farmhouse: a man's beaten forehead,
his opened lip.

In bars we watch your faces:
(they are like flower-heads); your
year-end news.
Asking things "What must I do?"

And are only a story of witnesses ready
this year again on the day before Epiphany.
Who might potter in a rented house,
tune the radio over south easterlies so:
"Behind the steering wheel," you will be saying, "sits
a blackened skeleton." And you
will listen.
"I had a son in nineteen forty seven
and I had him fostered,"
you will be saying,
and you listen to your sorrow.

"I flung my arms around him"
you say,
and you'll be listening.
You listening; you saying:
"He flung his arms around me."

I Remember

Andy Maranzi

I remember the echoes
The sun going down
One last time
I remember the dawn
Harsh and glistening
I remember the words
And I wasn't even listening
You see…
I remember

I remember the sea
The rhythm of waves
With no lifeline
I remember the priest
At my grandfather's christening
I remember the words
And I wasn't even listening
You see…
I remember

I remember the court
Of Arthur and Gwynne
In summertime
I remember the orchard
The apples and pears
I remember the words
And I wasn't even there
You see…
I remember

I remember your face
Like a pale opal moon
As we started to dine
I remember we swam

In the deep ocean blue
I remember the words
And I said them to you
You see...
I remember

Daisies

Maresa Sheehan

He loves me he loves me not
Petal-pulling play pulling people
Still plucking but skipping
Picking where I plonk in the field
He loves me he loves me not

Are we 'We'?

John Edmondson

To get	I'll get.	You'll get.	We'll get.
And give,	And give,	I'll give,	We'll give.
Forget,	Forget,	Forget,	Forget.
Forgive,	Forgive.	Forgive.	Forgive.
Would let	Please let	Could let	Now let
You live	Me live	You live	Us live
And love	And love	And love	And love
Again.	Again.	Again?	Again.

So

Which am I?

Which are you?

Are we 'We'?

Or nothing, then?

Relationship

Tim O'Halloran

We had been having the conversation on and off since that morning. You know the one, the conversation about the 'relationship'. After tea, she announced she was going out with her friends. I could use my time alone, she said, wait for it, "to think about our relationship."

We never talked about "our relationship." Very early on, I had told her how I hated the word, because to me it sounded too much like a mathematical function. It was a word without soul. She agreed. We were like that. It's like we agreed about everything.

Anyway, she used the 'R' word very deliberately all that day. It all seemed to come out of nowhere. We were out walking around Soho. I bought Exile in Main Street in a second-hand record shop. How could I resist? It was only £2. When we got back out on the street, she said "Where is this relationship going?" It was so sudden, I had no answer. Then, bizarrely she said "Why did you buy that?" pointing at the Stones album. I thought for a moment it was about sexism in rock music. Then I realised it couldn't be that, she had loads of Stones records. I had no idea what had brought all this on, so I tried as best I could to change the subject.

Anyway, that's why I ended up sitting up till the early hours, thinking about me and Magda. I had met her a few years before, in the Dog and Duck. We started to go out now and then. It was nothing heavy, we just saw each other once or twice a week. We were not 'exclusive' as she would put it. Though I thought the world of her, she was no poet.

I suppose I first realised just how I felt one night when I saw her with a guy from her work, drinking in the Dog and Duck. That struck me as odd, since the Dog and Duck was miles from where she worked. I left before she saw me. It was the strangest thing. My heart was pounding. I just hoped it was nothing serious with Accountant Boy. I told her that I loved her the very next time I saw her.

It's funny the way things develop. Just after that, I had a row with my landlord. I was down in the pub one night, going through the small ads, when the thought just struck her, out of the blue, that I should move into her flat. "Nothing heavy," she said, "it just makes sense, just think of all the money we would save." It just seemed so obvious I wondered why we hadn't thought about before.

This is what made the day's behaviour all the more strange. Because I had no idea what had brought all this on. For the rest of the day. I confined myself to meaningless platitudes. This only seemed to provoke her all the more.

I inserted my new purchase, alphabetically, with the other records. There was already a copy of Exile on Main Street. I wasn't surprised but I mentioned it anyway. She just looked at me in a way I had never seen before and said, "You would have known that, if you had asked."

Was this about wasting money? About £2? It crossed my mind that women just don't understand how guys like to collect things. It's about having something forever, it's not about having something in the here and now. I thought of a quote that someone had told me, how guys want an infinite number of things of no value, while women want just one thing of infinite value. I stopped myself in time, because I just knew Magda would guess I got it from it Maggie, my ex. I dodged that one didn't I? You have to be very sensitive when you are dealing with women. (Maggie's observation wouldn't really stand up in the January sales, would it? But that's not important right now.)

It was then that she suggested my need to reflect on our 'relationship'. Then she banged the door and left

At first I was relieved that she had left, she was being so unreasonable. Then a strange thing happened. I began to feel lonely. This was weird because she and I often went out on our own. Normally, if she went out without me, I opened a beer, relaxed and watched all those soap operas that she hated. That night it was different, I was not sure why. Maybe it was because she seemed to go out, not because she wanted to meet anyone in particular, but because she wanted to leave me alone. That seemed to make all the difference. If was as if being alone was not the problem, so much as why I was alone. It just wouldn't add up for me. I just felt, I don't know, a kind of hazy anxiety.

That was unexpected, because I had begun to believe that I was being smothered by Magda. We hardly went out anymore. It seemed like a long time since we had even been to the Dog and Duck. For the few weeks leading up to that day, I wasn't sure if I wasn't developing feelings for the girl with the pink spiky hair in the video shop. My heart no longer pounded when I came across Magda unexpectedly, as it had that night when I spied her in the Dog and Duck with Romeo the Accountant. In short the madness of new romance was gone. Without that madness what was left?

That night, sitting alone, a slow realisation seemed to come over me. I began to entertain the wholly new thought that the 'R' word might have a meaning. Now that I was forced to think about it, I could find no word to substitute for it. It occurred to me that, if there were no such thing as a relationship, we would spend our lives in a succession of doomed romances. Worse still, we would spend our lives in fruitless attempts to resurrect magical feelings that cannot be commanded.

It was like I was on a roll, because straight away another realisation came to me. To Magda, there was already only one record collection. When I bought that damned record, she saw into my mind, where there still seemed to be two record collections. It was that much and that little. How could I have missed that?

I began to think of what were the good and bad things about this new thing, this 'relationship'. It was bad thing that I no longer felt free to go down to the Dog and Duck every night. On the other hand, it was very good thing that I didn't feel I had to go down there every night. It was a bad thing to have to come home and have to listen to Magda listing all the trivial things that had happened to her that day. Then again, if I came home and she wasn't there, I would miss all those little stories. It seemed that the good and the bad were always two sides of the same coin. After a while I grew tired of these oppositions and started to drift off .

Then Magda arrived home. I was surprised that, though it was three in the morning, she seemed completely sober. Before she could say anything, I went down on one knee. "I figured it all out, Magda," I told her, "I've been a heedless fool. I don't know why I bought that stupid record. I never want us to part. Let's get married as soon as we can."

"It's about time," she said. "Everyone else seems to have figured it out ages ago. Our absence did not go unnoticed at the Dog and Duck. People had put two and two together. They were all asking me why we were holding off on the big announcement. What's all this about a record? I'm due in August, in case you have made other plans."

Maybe a relationship is best defined as a determination to travel together, though sometimes there is no clear communication, no map or no agreed destination. It's an understanding beyond all of these things. I shared this thought with Magda.

"That's just right," she said. "That's how I see it too, you and me together, hand in hand, walking into the sunset, except you are always stumbling and one step behind." Sometimes Magda has a cutting way about her.

Debs Dance

Pat McGrath

It's a long time since! It's almost impossible to recall through the mist of experience that has come and gone since then. And some experiences are very misty. Very cloudy... Maybe it's best left that way. But good or bad it has all conspired to bring me here. To this moment at the foot of the stairs.

1975. Exams coming soon. This will be it. Freedom around the corner. Finally out from under the thumb of Christian Brother oppression. Must study, but youth and other thoughts occupy that space. Who can concentrate on Pythagoras' theorem when you don't have a date for your own debs dance? The other guys in class are getting invitations almost daily to debs dances from all the local girls' schools. But hey! One thing at a time. Who should I ask? Who do I know? Oh of course! But what if she... No! Just grab the bull by the horns, so to speak. Right, that's it. Tomorrow on the bus I'll ask her if she would like to "accompany" me to my debs dinner dance in July ("Dress formal"). After all, this is a monumental event, a change in my life.

Well, with nerves steeled and determination bolstered, the question was asked. "I'd love to," she said. Suddenly all the apprehension seemed stupid. How do people do this kind of thing on a regular basis? I know that I would be a complete wreck to have to go through that too often. It must get easier with time. Anyway, back to Pythagoras. "The square on the hypoth..." Oh who cares? After all, I have a dance to go to.

The final weeks of school dragged. As always, the weather was probably some of the best we have had for years. The number of times I sat there watching clouds sweeping the weather across the sky. No wonder I never managed to get Pythagoras' theorem! How can I not be focused on this? Does everyone see this the same way? No, of course not. How can they? Everyone says that this is probably the most important time of my life but the devil on the shoulder says otherwise. Go outside. Play football. Who to believe? Relax. Don't panic.

Right! Let's just do this. First paper, English. How hard can it be?

We speak English, don't we? We think in English. We eat, sleep and drink English. Yeah! I can do this. The strangest two weeks followed. It almost seemed like an out of body experience and when people asked how I had done with such and such a paper, I really couldn't say. I had no guidelines. I had no inkling as to whether I had scored ninety-five percent or twenty-five percent and this was disturbing in the extreme. The exams came and the exams went. This, I have subsequently learned, will happen with or without my approval.

Three weeks to go. Two weeks. Don't forget to collect the suit. My first time to wear a proper dress suit. And a dickie bow. "The name's Bond, James Bond".... Who am I kidding? Mother and father both reassure. "You look gorgeous, son." I look like a right plank. Now the walk. I've been dreading this bit. The sister of a classmate has promised to drive us to the hotel. She will collect us at my date's house but I have to get there. The walk. Maybe nobody will notice if I'm quick and the gift of long legs suddenly has a purpose. Head down, step out and here we go. I have to get down this road before any of my mates see me like this. Dressed up like a peacock. "Take your time you clown," or you will arrive steaming like a racehorse.

Ding-dong! She answers the door and I meet a goddess whom I've only ever seen in her school uniform before. Wow! "You look good", was the best I could manage. As luck would have it my friend and his date arrived in the car with his sister, thereby avoiding that awkward shuffling time engaged in so often by the unsure. Greetings and compliments exchanged and we were off with anticipation born of the unknown. On arrival, I am aware of the flowers being worn on the dresses of most of the girls. Wondering what this is all about, I ask someone I trust to tell a reasonable semblance of the truth. It seems that tradition dictates that the boy should buy his date an orchid as a corsage on attending such functions. How did I not know that? Where did everyone else learn it? What a start to the evening. What embarrassment. Note to self... Buy orchid tomorrow. Let's hope that there aren't too many of those by the end of the night. Anyway, nothing I can do about that now.

That night the dinner dance seemed like the best dance ever held. Too much eating and too much drinking I suppose but we were out for the night and all too soon that night was gone and it was the early hours of the morning, and time to go home. But who could go home? Everyone wanted something to do, somewhere to go.

What time is it? Four of us ended up back at my date's house. We must have been here for quite a while telling stories, looking back at schooldays that had just come to an end, listening to music. The sun comes up and it's time to go. At least the walk from my date's house shouldn't attract too many stares. After all it is five o'clock in the morning. Standing now at the door saying goodnights and thank yous the gap between us closes and I get my first real kiss. Oh, I'd been kissed before, usually as a dare behind the bicycle sheds. But nothing like this. How could anything be that soft and taste so good? Floating now and not knowing what to say next. Or do. Ah well, in for a penny in for a pound. How did this work again?

I don't remember the walk home that morning but I do remember The Carpenters had been warbling in the background. I've always sort of liked The Carpenters since then.

That was a long time ago now as I wait at the foot of the stairs. Suddenly my breath is taken from me as I gawp helplessly at the vision now descending. "Say something, you fool!" I always thought that I would have some deep and meaningful words to say at a time like this. But what can I say as I watch my daughter approaching, fully prepared for her debs dance? "You look gorgeous, love, and make sure that he brings you an orchid."

Grace

Margaret Butler

Grace was always my favourite aunt. There was something different about her and indeed about both aunts on my father's side. Whereas my mother's sisters were plump, down to earth housewives with sensible names like Bridgie and Annie, the Kennedy sisters, Isobel and Grace, were, to my young eyes, glamorous and fascinating. The fact that their house – No. 38 – was only two doors down from ours, meant that I spent most of my childhood there.

Isobel worked in the fabric section of Clery's. Whenever my mother brought me into town we would always visit Clery's and I would watch in amazement as Isobel effortlessly lifted down huge bolts of colourful, shiny material and then proceed to measure and cut with a dexterity that was a joy to behold. For a long time working in Clery's was the height of my ambition.

The younger of the Kennedy sisters was Grace. Grace – what can I say about Grace except that she did what no other adult ever did when I was growing up – she treated me as an equal and I loved her for it. There were only ten years between us but to a seven year old, seventeen is an adult. Grace was different from anyone I ever knew. For a start she loved music – not the awful Irish music my parents used to listen to, but popular music like Elvis Presley and Buddy Holly. When she was given a transistor radio for her birthday, she used to tune in to Radio Luxembourg every evening and I became her jiving partner. By the time I was eight I could jive with the best of them.

Grace loved dancing. She also loved make-up and clothes, and when what she earned as a typist didn't stretch far enough, she was full of enterprising ideas to make money. Her first money making idea had started way back when she was only a kid herself. We lived in Bath Avenue, not far from Lansdowne Road. There were fewer cars in those days and many people cycled to the grounds. Kids on our road had always minded the bikes for a few pence, but Grace soon cornered the market. No. 38 had a side garden and this became the parking lot. It was a highly organised operation. Grace used a ticket system and my job was to arrange the bikes in numerical order so that each one could be retrieved without having to clamber over all the others.

People knew they could trust Grace and we made quite a bit of money. The local sweet shop received most of my earnings but Grace saved up hers and bought a second hand sewing machine. Aunt Isobel could get cheap remnants of material in Clery's, so after a few false starts, Grace was soon supplying friends and neighbours with the latest fashions and earning a tidy sum. She planned to go to the Grafton Academy at night to study dress designing. The bike minding business passed to me and I roped in my brother as a junior partner.

Every weekend Grace went dancing and I loved watching her get ready. She would put rollers in her hair on Saturday afternoon and later she would brush it out so that it fell to her shoulders, all wavy and bouncy. Sometimes she would back comb it and put it up in a beehive style. I didn't like this as much but she said it was all the rage.

She applied her make-up with intense concentration. First she would put on pan stick foundation and blend it in carefully. Then would come her eye shadow – always blue or green – and applied with her finger tip. When she was satisfied, out would come the little block of mascara. She would spit on the brush, rub it round the hardened mascara and then apply it to her eyelashes, curling them upwards so that they looked enormous. Lastly, she put on lipstick. Coral Pink was her favourite shade and once applied she would place a paper hankie between her lips and press them firmly together. She would then dress in one of her own creations – usually a figure hugging dress that came just above the knee, step into what I considered to be dangerously high heels, give a twirl and say to her reflection in the mirror "Knock 'em dead, kid."

Sometimes disaster would strike and she would find a ladder in her stockings at the last minute. Then it would be my job to race to the corner shop to buy a pair of Majorca Tan nylons for one and nine pence. I always got to keep the three-pence change.

It was inevitable that one of these Saturday night excursions would lead to Grace meeting a boyfriend, and when she brought home Billy Campbell I thought he was gorgeous. With his dark hair combed back in a quiff, he looked a bit like Cliff Richard. Aunt Isobel though was not impressed and neither was my father.

"A right Bobby Dazzler that fella – it'll all end in tears. Mark my words."

But anyone could see that Billy thought the world of Grace. He would bring her flowers and chocolates and was always holding open doors for her. Once he borrowed his father's car and brought her down to

Glendalough for the day. Another time he even allowed Grace's friend Julie, who was a right drip, to tag along on a date, because Grace told him she was recovering from a broken romance and was feeling miserable. When my father heard this he said that Julie Dempsey was a long streak of misery to begin with and how any poor fellow had put up with her for a night let alone a few months was a mystery to him.

No, Billy was a decent generous man and anyone could see that Grace was in love. Everything was Billy this and Billy that and she never talked now about her plans to go to the Grafton Academy. When she brought me into town now, instead of spending time looking at patterns and material, we would gaze in the window of McDowells the Happy Ring House and imagine what engagement ring Billy would buy her. She fancied the solitaires but I liked the rings with one big diamond in the middle and a little one either side.

That winter I got scarlet fever and spent three weeks in hospital. Only my parents were allowed to visit and so I didn't see Grace for some time. When I did see her I was shocked. All the sparkle had gone out of her. She didn't bother any more with her hair and make-up and when I suggested turning on Radio Luxembourg and doing the new dance – the Twist – she just wasn't interested. It turned out that Billy had dumped her. Not only that but he had taken up with her friend Julie Dempsey. My father said that was good enough for him – no man deserved to be happy all his life.

Aunt Isobel talked about other fish in the sea but there was no consoling Grace. She was miserable. I seemed to be the only one that felt really angry with Billy Campbell. How dare he treat Grace like that? How dare he take away the one fun-loving person in my life? One day when I was coming home from town with my mother I saw him and Julie Dempsey arm in arm, laughing and joking with each other and I got so mad I roared out the only insult I could think of.

"Louser!"

My mother was appalled and yanked me home by the arm.

A few weeks later Grace announced that she was going to England. She was fed up with her job, fed up with Dublin and anyway London was where it was all happening. Surprisingly, neither my father nor Aunt Isobel objected to the idea, and so it was on a cold Saturday in March that we found ourselves down at Dun Laoghaire pier as Grace prepared to board the mail boat. We were an odd group. I was bawling my eyes out, while the adults, Grace included, all spoke with a cheerfulness that was false even to my childish ears. But when it came to the actual moment of goodbye, everyone was crying, even my father, something I had never seen before.

For days afterwards I moped around the house. Even visiting No. 38 did nothing to lift my spirits because without Grace the house was strangely quiet. No music blared from the radio, there were no patterns and bits of material lying about and when I went up to her bedroom the only thing on her dressing table was an empty tube of Coral Pink lipstick.

Two weeks later, a letter arrived for me from London. This was the first letter I ever received and I have kept it to this day. The envelope, with the red English stamp, looked so important, that I held it as if it were a sacred thing and only opened it when I had scrutinised it carefully. There were two pages of white lined notepaper filled with Grace's neat handwriting. She had a job in an office that was just as boring as the one back home but it would do for a start. She had made friends with another Irish girl called Linda and they were staying in a hostel for the time being since flats and bedsits were expensive and they had to save up money for a deposit. When they were settled she might invite me over for a holiday. I was wild with excitement. Imagine going to see Buckingham Palace, the Tower of London, Madam Tussauds!

Over the next few months I received more letters from Grace but she never seemed to be any nearer getting her own place. Then out of the blue I arrived home from school one day and there she was sitting at our kitchen table. I was over the moon to see her but I have to admit that there was a part of me quite disappointed to learn that she was home for good because now I would never have that holiday in London. The array of sweets on the table – Spangles, Mars bars and Milky Ways – went some way to cheer me up.

The relationship between Grace and me was never the same after her sojourn in London. When she came back she was more like the other adults in my life. Indeed sometimes I thought she was even more serious and solemn. The ritual of the Saturday night dance was gone and she hardly ever did any dressmaking. Two months after her twenty-first birthday she emigrated to Boston where she met and married a big softie called Charlie Stevenson. He was no oil painting but he was one of the good guys. My father grew to like him a lot.

A few years ago I moved house and in the major decluttering that this involves, I came across some old letters. One of them had a red English stamp. I re-read that letter and somehow I knew then that all that talk of the hostel, the boring office job, the plans to get a flat just didn't ring true. I went to the computer and googled the address: Birdhurst Lodge, Croyden, London.

The entry was concise:

"Up to the late 1960's Birdhurst Lodge was a home for unmarried mothers..."

I looked again at Grace's letter and I wept. I wept for Grace and for all that might have been.

That Time in January.

Thomond Gill

I stood on the white sand,
higher up.
And watched as she played in the waves
of his clear blue eyes.
Dancing. Delighted. Laughing
off the cold that hit her,
Now and then.
Blinded by the sun
she could not see
any deeper, but I did.
I stood by
and let him take her.
I waited
as she waded
through her murky waters
and watched her emerging.
Bitter. Cold. And blue.

Everybody's Got Somebody

Conor Ferguson

He was six-foot-two with red hair, and certainly no oil painting. More of a collage. It was the beard. It made him look like one of those Amish people in that film. It was almost like a barrier.

But that night at the pub quiz, there was something in him that cut deep into her long years of loneliness and wanting the world to mind its own business. (You can give up your life to crying but, she learned, it does nothing any good.) She forgot about her uneven features and her hard, ugly past.

For him, the dying sister had been an excuse to not even think about love, or having it off, or that. He knew no-one in Dublin, nor liked any of them either. Until the pub quiz (a blind date, kindly schemed by the gang in work). She kept laughing and he didn't know why. But it felt nice.

He walked her home, accidentally taking her hand, as if it was his sister's. But this one was soft and warm and he didn't want to let it go. They saw each other every day since. Finally, he stayed the night in her place.

Both were nervous, but the second time they did it it felt so fucking amazing she nearly made a show of herself. The bad times flew out of them, and he knew, "I'll die with this woman's name on my lips." And the next day the beard was history.

No One Home

Kate Neil

He was still drinking.
She watched him through the deep aching in her heart.
Surrounded by admirers,
He was in his element.
They were laughing hard at his jokes.
The ones she had heard so often.
It was the unique perfection of his delivery.
And oh how they loved his 'Irish Brogue.'

They were re-filling the glass for him now –
Getting closer – patting him on the back.
Everyone wanting a piece of him.
Laughing with him all the way.
Later they would laugh at him
drifting back to their whispering corners.

He was almost alone now.
Laughing too loud at his own jokes
The occasional curse thrown in for good measure.
They didn't like that,
This tight Boston beehive.
It wasn't in their plan.
He was supposed to entertain.

He would become hyper-sensitive then,
Sensing the disapproval,
Feeling inadequate.
One more and he would become aggressive.
Would become intent on getting drunk.
Like a man who had no one to go home to.
When had she become
no one?

The Favoured Child

Maresa Sheehan

He's a cliché from some stage Irish play
Stirring the fifth spoon of sugar in his tea.
"Well Maurice, how are you keeping?"
"You have me now!" he delivers with detachment.
"It's a fright to God you don't know your own brother!"
The black sticky tar keeps rolling
like their mother in the grave.

What's going on in his mind?
This black deep bog oak of a man
that was once the dewdrop
of his mother's morning
the finest bull weanling
in his father's herd.
He could discuss the Tsars of Russia,
the plot of a play, the uselessness
of a political team.
This crab apple of his mother's blind sight
is now just stupid and mean.

He got the place – the favoured child
lack of critical praise the vice
that overturned, squeezed the twig
into this twisted dark ugly bog oak.
It's interesting and attractively odd
to consider the forces and see pages
that made this sod of a man.
Up close it burns cold.

The house is a sty, stubbornness and arrogance
sinking him to the bottom of a boghole
with layered sides of rotton vegetation –
thrown out the back door by his mother?
Or in the ground for years before him?

Who cares? They all say he was miserable
but not ignorant, if that's consolation to the few
gathered round left looking into the hole.

"I must call back to you some day Maurice!"
"The passage is gone very rough,
you would only ruin your car."
"Were you selling a few cattle at the mart?"
"I was but the price was bad,
I better head on and get home before the dark."

As if he liked the light
alone, sad, favoured child.

Goose Steppes

Eobhan O'Brien

At present my life is a patchwork quilt stitched by an arthritic colour-blind neurotic with limited thread. Yours is a Siberian white goose down comforter like the one we bought last week. "Like sleeping in angel's wings." The saleswoman placed it reverentially in its box – laying a well-loved relative to rest. Somewhere a flock of geese menacingly streaking, maverick fowl – a *gulag* stripped for our night's rest. You are not amused – forcing a smile over your espresso, finger crooked to circle a full-stop to such nonsense. This is our first month living together – my old bachelor flat and your minimalist apartment conjoined in an aberration of fraying crochet and sharp-ended stainless steel.

Now my boxes merge with yours – they jostle as we do; unused to sharing space. Your morning routine jars. A truce is still in operation over the TV since blood was almost drawn last weekend. I love a good whodunit but seven hours of "Poirot"?

It's the bedroom where the biggest struggles take place. Your half of the room has one three-legged stool artfully stacked with unthumbed well-regarded tomes. On my side of the divide a tumultuous crowd dive-bomb and quiver for attention. We haven't spoken about this yet – it is the elephant in the room we trip over.

I find it difficult to sleep in your bed – most nights I creep to the room where my faithful futon lives and lay low to the floor; the familiar bumps cushioning me into drowsiness. You are not happy about this – a rejection. In the evening you delay at the office – work commitments now vital. I am torn between wanting you home immediately and enjoying the solitude. Usually I resentfully anticipate the key in the door. The physical reality of being within these walls somehow makes me think I'm one step nearer to death. Unfortunately I cannot voice these thoughts to you as you shuffle through the debris of my life, catching your toe and swearing under your breath.

I'm smoking up the chimney when I hear your key in the door. My job is quiet now until the post-Christmas rush – people always return to counselling after the season of goodwill with gaping wounds. They have been betrayed by the gloss and pomp, they have realized that they are now in the same place albeit with more unwanted goods to pack to the back of the cupboard.

Your nose is in the air like a bloodhound, "Thought you were on the gum?" "I am, in between smokes," I gesture to the dried up piece of pizza. "There's some left." You head to the kitchen. "I'll have a salad – did you think anymore about what to tell the parentals?" This is your main concern these days – the story of our meeting and how to disguise it into a spirited yet romantic tale that shows us both in a good light. I light up. "I'll tell mine you're another one of my clients unable to resist a good listener." You slam the fridge door punctuating, "And am I?" "Jesus, of course not... we'll just tell them we met at a mutual friend's wedding." I know we're about to have the details conversation – whose wedding, how do we know them, where did they go on honeymoon – "I'm heading out for some air – do you want anything?" I throw my jumper over my head and out – just catching your request for beer.

It's not the ideal, but people meet in all sorts of scenarios. You came to work through some obsessive compulsive tendencies; we joke about it – of all the couches, in all the shrinks' offices in all the world. You were fragile – feathery blonde hair– pale as a boiled bone. It crept up on me – as you progressed I became fixated. Reading your notes obsessively; gleaning for clues – for something I had missed. Citing new working arrangements I recommended you see another therapist in my building – and timed my departures to coincide with the end of your appointments. Two years later here we are – you have made enormous progress and I'm the one smoking up a chimney in a house I view as a vice-grip on all imagined freedoms.

The power paradigm has shifted, according to my therapist, while I picture him in his underwear. He tells me all the things I already know – all the things I tell my own clients. We sit for an hour – often in silence – as we play the game of who will crack first and speak. I stop off at the pharmacy to pick up more vitamins – I need to build myself up, get fit, get a hobby, meet new people, paint that masterpiece, volunteer – failing that I need to clear a path from my bed to the door to ease my exit.

Heading home I almost forget your beer – I buy a side-dish of ice cream and wafers, feeling a rush to the head. This is your favourite combination; it is bought in homage to the old you – the you that kept me late at the library researching ethics, the you before you found your quirks troublesome. I need to fall in love with the new edition. You greet me at the door – an odd expression on your face; I present you with the bag – a kiss on your rosy cheek. "I've something to tell you – I was at the doctors today." All the terrible scenarios rush to the front of my mind

– death beds, protracted illness, my life without you in it. I feel sick, faint – coming back you say it again "...a baby." With this I hand you the blank cheque of my affections.

I Think You Mean Kiss You Good-Bye

Róisín McDermott

She began to dream about him. Long broken dreams. Nightmare scenarios where everything keeps shifting. One night she dreamed that she and Elvis and Jane Eyre were wandering the moors together; she knew they were on the moors, even though, in the surreal landscape of the dream, they were surrounded by the Mourne Mountains. They could hear Mr Rochester calling, this ghostly voice in the distance, but when they fought their way to him through the swirling mists, they found, not Mr Rochester, but Seán McNamara. She would wake from these dreams, confused, disoriented, thinking for a nanosecond that the night of the GAA Dress Dance had never, in fact, happened.

Gloria, crumpled and pale, cried into her boiled egg and told her mother never to mention Seán McNamara's name again. "And turn that bloody thing off," she pleaded, as Elvis crooned achingly from the radio on the shelf behind her, "*Is your heart filled with pain, shall I come back again...*" On the bus to Belfast, huddled into her sheepskin coat, she cried all the way through the cold dawn, the streaming windows and hoar frost fields a parallel to her misery; Joe, the bus conductor, eyeing her with dismay as he whirred his ticket machine and handed out tickets to the usual Monday morners. Through Katesbridge, on to Loughbrickland, a dripping sign proclaimed "Brontë Country". Oh God, Jane Eyre, you were well spawned in this godforsaken landscape; what legacy of melancholy did Patrick Brontë, born and reared in this vale of tears, bring to his children, and through them, for posterity, to the likes of you? Donegall Square at last, down Fountain Street, into the creaking lift, dry your eyes, you silly cow, he'll be back, over to your desk, that's it, sit down, busy, busy, on Her Majesty's service, he'll phone on Wednesday like he always does, he will, yes he will.

She could hardly bear to admit it, but last night Seán McNamara had blown her out like a light. Young men and women didn't dump one another in those days, they used gentler euphemisms, but it all meant the same thing in the end: you were gone, kaput, no point pretending. "Gloria," he'd said to her, pulling in outside her house, keeping his hands on the steering wheel of his Hillman Minx, after the GAA Dress Dance in the Mourne View Hotel. "Gloria, I swear to Jesus I can't put up with your carry-on any longer, flirting with every man in sight. In the name of God! I have had it up to here. Enough is enough. I don't want to see you anymore. And don't be kissing me good-night," he turned his beautiful blond head and his slightly drunk-looking dicky bow away from her as she leaned towards him. "Or I'll never be able to leave you." Gloria was shocked, no, Gloria was appalled, but a gut feeling told her that the middle of the night, with that face on him, wasn't the time for a drag-out, knock-down argument about why she'd spent half the night chatting up Peter Quinn – the gorgeous Peter Quinn. She remembered now that somewhere between the turkey and ham with glazed carrots and *pommes de terre* and the sherry trifle, Seán had stopped speaking to her altogether. This was a case for a bit of space, Gloria decided. She manipulated her long, slender frame out of the Hillman Minx in her new floor-length scarlet dress, the orchid he had brought her tilted tipsily on her bosom. He didn't look at her. Didn't look at her at all.

There was no word from him, not a beep. Every time the phone rang, on Her Majesty's desk, or on the landing outside the flat in Eglantine Avenue, Gloria's heart stopped, but it was never Seán McNamara on the other end. Elvis, meanwhile, was climbing to the top of the charts, crooning, swooning, unbearable: *Are you lonesome to-night, do you miss me tonight, are you sorry we drifted apart?* Could Gloria possibly have had more bad luck than to finally piss Seán McNamara off the week one of the greatest love-songs of all time hit the airwaves?

At night, in the flat, Gloria cried and fretted and went over everything a thousand times, until Eileen and Maggie wished that Seán McNamara had never been born. Well that wasn't strictly true; of course they felt for her, but secretly they were glad that it was Gloria's turn to suffer (their own romances going quite well at the moment, praise the Lord), for it had long been recognised that all three of them were never happy in love at the same time. Their little flat wrapped itself around them, enclosed them as they talked and talked at the kitchen table, or hunched round the fire drinking mugs of Maxwell House and smoking Benson and Hedges, trying to put some sort of shape on Gloria's tragedy, for that's what it was – hardly of Brontë proportions – but a tragedy nevertheless to Gloria. The part where he asks her not to kiss him goodnight was naturally the focus of their discussion and for the hundredth time the girls told her that, yes, it looked like he definitely fancied her (which was something to hold onto in her despair), but that he might have come to the end of his tether, so to speak. After a week she found she couldn't say his name; it was 'he' or 'him', but she couldn't say the name 'Seán', as if by not articulating that sweetest of names the loss of him would seem less real.

After two weeks of silence Gloria could bear it no longer. All the excuses had been made: he'd broken his leg and couldn't walk to the phone box: he had laryngitis and couldn't speak: he had written to her and the letter had gone astray – letters went astray all the time, didn't they? She decided to take the bull by the horns and write to him, to the cold, grey, seaside town where he lived. Her friends said, well, what had she to lose, while somehow implying that she might not have a lot to gain either. She felt better after she made this decision, empowered, I suppose you would say, more in control. In retrospect, it probably wasn't a great idea to base the main thrust of her argument for getting back together on the immortal line from "Lady Chatterley's Lover", then being read to titters of shock in all the flats in Belfast. "What we had together is met only once in this life", she wrote, or something equally awful along those lines. "You can't send him that," shrieked Eileen, "he'll recognise it, for Christ's sake!" But to Gloria it was such a perfect line, encapsulating everything she felt for Seán McNamara, that she sent it anyway, and the minute the letter disappeared into the post box she was seized with agonies of shame at how foolish she would look if he had read Lady Chatterley. Oh Christ, what a disaster.

She was never to find out. He replied within the week, putting paid to all speculation of accidents that might have befallen him. Clearly he was in the best of health and in acerbic, unforgiving mood, the envelope in his large square handwriting staring at her from the little table in the hall in Eglantine Avenue, waiting for her like a life sentence when she came home from work; a cold, disapproving look about it, sitting there, Gloria thought, like she knew in her heart what was inside. Afterwards she could never recall exactly what was in the letter; it was so painful that she crumpled it in a ball and stuffed it in her handbag. But the gist of it was that he had thought and prayed for guidance on the matter of their "starting anything" again and his decision was that he could not take her back. It was the mention of prayer that convinced Gloria she had lost the battle, for she knew how ill-equipped she was to compete with the Almighty. She had asked him to meet with her (Gloria figured that if she could get him back to the kissing stage she was away on a hack, but give the man some credit, he knew that too), and he said no, he would not be seeing her again. There was no indication that he had made a connection between Gloria's use of language and that of Lady Chatterley and her lover.

Gloria stood for several moments, or was it several years, beside the little hall table, holding her handbag with the crumpled letter inside, not moving, hardly breathing; but at some point she brought herself slowly to the stairs, and began the climb towards the rest of her life without Seán McNamara.

Elvis reached number one that night, crooning and weeping his way across the city.

Friends rallied, and Elvis was turned off the minute he opened his mouth, but the whole of Belfast couldn't be in on the conspiracy to silence him and she was often exposed to blasts of melancholy which made her very soul ache: Tell me dear are you lonesome tonight? Lonesome? She wanted to die. She knew why Charlotte Brontë had Jane laying down on the moors in her anguish over Mr Rochester, almost succumbing to "the friendly numbness of death". What else would the reader expect but at least a bit of an effort on Jane's part to shuffle off? Of course Jane didn't die, because Charlotte had to write another 120 pages or so, but it was touch-and-go for a while out there on the heath. Gloria thought it would have been so easy to get into bed with her smelling salts (or whatever women with the vapours used these days) and just fade away, like they did in Victorian times, instead of wading through this dark, heavy fog of sadness, day in, day out. Sometimes she could hardly bear it. It seemed as if her world had flattened and dimmed, the colour all lea§ched from faces and buildings; winter inside and outside her head. News filtered to her that he was drinking too much – her spirits lifted – she imagined him, sodden, missing her, or that he had been seen at a GAA match in Casement Park chatting to the glamorous Marcella Murphy (full of herself, brother played midfield for Derry) – back down in the dumps – he'd be engaged before she knew it. She found she could say his name again, tripping it off her lips without the slightest bother – "that bastard McNamara."

Elvis stayed at number one for six weeks.

Of course we all know, all of us who've been through this heartbreak thing, that Gloria didn't die, any more than Jane Eyre died. Time dragged her along in its wake, for sure, as it will do whatever frame of mind a body is in, and someplace between the Orchid Ballroom on Wednesday nights, Maxim's on Thursdays and the Operatic Society on Fridays, Gloria discovered the truth of the old Irish proverb: "Never run after a man or a bus, there'll be another one along in a minute." And so, a year later saw her leaving her new haunt, the Saturday night rugby dance in the Ulster Arms, with a rowdy crowd of new friends. She almost passed him, sitting inside the door, in his suit, all by himself, two o'clock in the morning, looking a bit worse for the wear. "Aren't you going to kiss me goodnight?" he said, holding his hand out to her, and Gloria, taken by surprise, laughing, confident, being called to hurry up by her new loud friends, replied, "I think you mean kiss you good-bye, don't you, Seán?" and tossed her red locks at him and left him sitting there, uncomfortable, out of place in rugby territory, as she swept out into the night, laughing too loudly, skirts swirling behind her.

Oh sweet victory for Gloria, or so it seemed at the time: a settling of scores; a having had the last word. Fuck him! Now when Elvis sang about parlours being empty and bare, and did she picture him there, she gave him the fingers. She was elated; it was enough to know he still wanted her. She wondered if injured pride at being rejected had been the cause of much of her heartache. She remembered why she flirted with other men when she was with Seán McNamara: he was so bloody quiet and moody he drove her crazy, sitting there all night, not a word out of him. But still. He was gorgeous and could he kiss. Jesus!

Time passed, as it does, and Gloria went away and lived her life and came back now and then. And across this arc of time she sometimes met him in company, or raised a glass across a room; all mannered politeness and bright smiles but a tension between them like a kiss waiting to be kissed. Except that now he buys orchids for someone else and another someone brings roses to Gloria. And in all their lives they are never to be alone again.

And so, that would have been the end of it, another romance that didn't work out, so what? Except that fate played another cruel trick on Gloria. Elvis died and became immortal; well, a lot of people were convinced he didn't die at all, so great was their anguish, and Elvis kept on turning up in bars and airports all around the world, just like he always did, or so it was said. Forests of column inches were written, endless documentaries researched, PhD's negotiated on the phenomenon of the King who would not die. "Are you lonesome tonight" was re-released in every compilation and combination imaginable: "The Best of Elvis: Heartbreak Hotel; Elvis, the Greatest Hits", and every year, on his anniversary, a newer and greater album was launched. There was to be no escape. Even Gloria saw the irony in it, but all the same, down through the years, when that old yearning song crept up on her in the oddest of places, like a mountain-top café in Austria, or a marble tiled courtyard in Cyprus, it still left her wistful and sad. And many a night, at home, she would hear it unexpectedly across the airwaves of a late night radio station, she, glass in hand, lonely, the voice and the words transcending time, the past a present where she didn't want to be.

She heard one night, late, that Seán McNamara was dead. She moved to a window to stare hard into the blackness of the universe, then raised her glass to him across the great divide and blew a kiss into the void where he had gone.

It began to seem as if everyone connected to her was dead. Her mother gone; Joe the bus-conductor's ticket machine silent; Eileen and Maggie passing away within a year of each other, and the man who brought her roses for forty years keeling over one night in the middle of the nine o'clock news. She could feel her world emptying and shrinking, as if the soundtrack of her life were being rewound, discordant, out of tune, back past all the dead people, back into the womb, to be expelled again, screaming, alone.

After the dreams began she woke one morning to the sound of her own screams, reincarnated into a world she didn't recognise, pieces of a past life remembered, large stretches of it drifting away from her, the dreams lasting for days, or maybe years. Memories and shadows came and went inside her head, losing each other, intersecting, criss-crossing; reality a country she didn't live in anymore. The only constant was a kiss, which hovered in her consciousness, waiting, suspended over a void which could have been heaven, but might just as well have been hell.

Her room looks out on the Mournes; the slopes as purple and beautiful as anything she has seen in her long travels. It is summer now, always summer, warm and dreamlike; all the snow gone from the peaks, the hoar frost melted from the fields. Mr Rochester comes often to see her; he brings orchids and teases her about how beautiful she looks in her scarlet dress ("that wee red dress," he calls it). Jane Eyre comes with her husband, Seán McNamara. It pleases Gloria that Jane had that vision which brought her back across the Mournes to Seán; he looks well and his sight is returning. Jane is radiant; her red hair bright under her bonnet. The singer, Elvis Presley, is not allowed to visit, although he tries to come into her room every day. She sees his face at the window, hears him singing always the same old thing: *"Is your heart filled with pain, shall I come back again, tell me dear are you lonesome tonight"*. What a strange old-fashioned song; she could almost swear she'd heard it somewhere before.

The nurses smile and tell her not to listen: "Just some old ditty from the past," they say, "sure it never really caught on."

Bavarian Dream

Kate Neil

I want to go back there
when the wildflowers are in bloom
and the sun is lighting up the meadows.
I want to breathe the pure air,
taste the sweet cream, the crisp white wine,
hear the mellow notes of cow-bells.
I want to dance – that funny folk dance –
and laugh with the Lederhosen-clad men
in their feathered hats.
I want to admire those strong women
who bring us steins of beer as big as my face, and sip it slowly
as we watch the shadows creeping over the purple mountains.
I want to wander home through the fields,
share our dreams with the star-filled night,
feel the warmth of your strong hand in mine.
I want to snuggle under the goose-down quilt,
a kleines kopfkissen at my neck,
your body wrapped around mine, and drift gently
to that peaceful place, where we breathe in rhythm.

That Day

Grace Garvey

Passers-by glanced at Anna Kearney as she made her way down Main Street with her three boys in tow. The women wondered if the two smallest were twins and the men… well, the men were less focused on the curly-haired cherubs than on the willowy figure of their mother with her distracted air.

"Where are we going?" asked Kieran the eldest, pulling out of his mother. "You'll see," said Anna, wondering if she should let him in on the surprise but deciding not to. It was their father's idea and she'd been against it from the start. She figured she'd be the one who'd wind up paying for it. But as usual he'd worn her down 'til she said yes.

"Are we nearly there? I'm tired," wailed the four-year-old Matthew, stopping in the middle of the footpath. Anna swivelled on the spiky heel of her knee-length boot. "Do you want me to bring you back to the car and leave you there?" "No," he mumbled, his lower lip trembling. "Well then, get a move on," she said picking up speed.

They crossed into Shop Street and walked past Molloy's. Anna remembered when Molloy's had a bakery and her mother would send her there to buy fresh batch. The shop smelt warm and homely and Mr Molloy would give her a lollipop for being a good girl. She would dangle the green plastic bag in the crook of her elbow and wander up to Sheridan's at the top of the street. There in the snug her mother would be having 'a small one' with Kitty Comer. "Don't tell your father," she would say, pouring ginger ale onto Scotch.

Just then, Matthew spotted his father getting out of a car across the street. "Look there's Daddy," he yelped, his baby face breaking into a smile. "Not now, we don't have time," said Anna grabbing him by the hand. "Daddy, daddy," he called out, twisting away from his mother's tug. Jim Kearney waved and began to cross the road weaving through the traffic. "How're my little soldiers," he said ruffling Matt's hair and putting his arms around the others. "We're off to get a surprise," Adrian, the five-year-old said, hopping from one foot to the other. "And what kind of a surprise would that be?" asked Jim, winking at Anna. "Mammy won't tell us," all three chimed, looking up at him expectantly. "Well that's why it's a surprise," said their father laughing, clipping them on the legs.

"How're you feeling now," Jim asked, turning towards Anna, his voice quiet. "Ah, a bit better, I slept after you left," she answered, seeing the concern cloud his face. "I stuck the muppets in front of the video." She laughed, and he felt reassured. "I'll be home around seven, so give me a ring if you need anything. This lot will be up to high-doh." Anna rolled her eyes and they shared a smile at this. He kissed her before turning to the boys. "Alright fellas, see ye later. Be good now." "Bye, byeeee," the boys chorused, as their father ambled back towards his office. Anna watched him cross the street, his big frame moving in long strides. "He looks good in a suit," she thought, seeing him disappear with a wave.

"I know where we're going," said Kieran, as they turned right at the church. Anna looked at her first-born and thought how like his father he was becoming. "I do, I do, we're going to the park, aren't we?" he said nodding. He had Jim's eyes, gentle and intelligent, and Anna worried about him sometimes. He'd been in an awful lot of scrapes lately for one who didn't play football. When she asked him recently how he tore his jacket at school, he couldn't answer. Then, after thinking about it, he looked away and said softly: "it was just horseplay."

"No, we're not going to the park, smarty-pants, but you're getting warm." The park looked inviting all the same. If Jim were here, he'd go stomping through the crisp leaves and chase the boys to the swings. But Anna felt she could sink onto the nearest bench and never get up. She wanted to sit by the climbing frame and stare at the sky. "Maybe later though."

They turned into a laneway and stopped outside a boarded-up shop about halfway down. "Is this it?" one of the boys asked, as if it had to be a mistake. Anna was trying to figure out where the doorbell was. No doorbell, no knocker, she tapped on the window with her car keys. She put her ear to the heavy door and could hear commotion coming closer. "Hold on, hold on," she heard a man say, before shuffling a metal bar along the door. "Ah, Marie, there you are." "No, it's Anna, Mr Maloney," she reminded him, well used to people confusing her with her sister.

"Come in, come in," he said throwing open the double doors. Two Alsatian dogs bounded out and the smaller boys clutched their mother. Inside was exactly as she remembered. The long bar counter stretched along the far wall, lined with tall wooden stools. Beer taps protruded over the counter, crying out for their glory days. It felt like it was only yesterday since the place was humming with chat.

"How's Marie?" Mr Maloney inquired. He'd always had a soft spot for Anna's sister who'd been best friends with Una Maloney. "I haven't seen her for a long time…" his voice tailed off. No, not since she was eighteen and took off, Anna thought. "Ah you know Marie," she said. "She always falls on her feet."

"In we go, in we go." Anna still got the giggles at the way he said everything twice. They went through a door down a narrow corridor and out into the back yard. "Are there rats here, Mammy?" Matthew whispered. "No, of course not, silly," she said following Mr Maloney into an outhouse where they used to store grain. It was here herself and Marie had had their first cigarette. She could still see her sister choking on the first puff and running to the hosepipe for a drink.

It was dark inside and the stone walls hushed them into silence. The ground was strewn with bits of hay, and it felt safe and warm. There was noise coming from the far corner but it was hard to say what it could be. "This way, this way," said Mr Maloney leading them towards the muffled sound. An area had been walled off with a low makeshift fence. Matthew peered in and grinned. "We're getting a dog, Mammy, aren't we?"

Huddled together on a bed of straw was a litter of pups with their mother. They had long floppy ears and golden red coats. They made a low mewling sound and looked as if they'd just had a good feed. "Can we have that one, can we?" Adrian said pointing to the one who'd taken a few steps towards the visitors wagging its tiny tail. Anna looked at the boys. For once, they were all agreed on what they wanted. "Right so," said Mr Maloney picking up the chosen pup. "A little girl ye've got yerselves," he said, holding her out so they could see.

They said goodbye to Mr Maloney and set off back for the car. The boys were over-excited and wanted to stop every few minutes for a look. Anna would set down her straw bag at regular intervals and let them take it in turns to give their new pet a rub. The walk back took no time at all and before they knew it, they were on Main Street again. "Oh no, it's going to rain," said Kieran who hated his head getting wet. And sure enough, a light shower turned to downpour just as he reached for his hood.

"In here," Anna said, stopping at a roomy doorway facing onto the square. They huddled together and looked out at the rain. "This place smells funny," Matthew said scrunching his nose. "That's because they keep robbers inside," said Adrian who'd heard all about the station from Sergeant Finnegan's son, Jack. "Rain rain, go away," Matthew yodelled, but the sky wasn't listening. "OK, wait here and I'll go and get the car," Anna said hoisting up an umbrella and dashing off.

The traffic was heavy and slow as Anna turned onto the square. She edged her way up until at last, she could see the boys in the doorway lit by stark white light. The two younger ones were on their hunkers, dipping into the tall straw bag. Kieran alone looked anxious, staring into street. The lights turned amber and then green. The squad car in front curved around to the left. Anna took one last look at the alcove full of curls and shot straight ahead.

She pressed her foot on the pedal and sped through the old part of town. Soon she had a clear road and the houses disappeared. Rain rattled down on the windowscreen and her tears fell in floods.

Gift

Clare Farrell

Buried at the bottom of a drawer
I find a crumpled hand-drawn card
with a lopsided heart in muddy pink
and the letters of your name spelled out
singly and with serious deliberation.
And when you gave it to me
it was as if you handed me
that whole ten minutes of your life
when nothing else intruded
on the careful spelling of your name
and the outline of your long pink heart
and the wait for it to dry
and the thought of bringing it to me.

Restricted Visiting

Eobhan O'Brien

This is the last time.
Our conversation tar-coated.
All paid out and spent,
the sum total of this partnership.

Your coffee sipping irritates
I itch to slap you down,
resist only with the fullstop in sight.

Disinfected: this our last togetherness,
funnelled through this corridor.
Then siphoned out into bite-sized bitterness.

If this were a movie
illness would glue us together.
Now visiting hours
are over.

Old Man
Conn Redmond

Eighty-nine years old, a pipe smoker, he'd sit close to the fire and tell me life straight. "She was nice," he said one night in November, the two of us around a warm hearth. He always looked relaxed, a tall well-built man: legs crossed, traditional blue suit, white shirt with frayed collar, a tie loose around his neck. He spoke again. "You shouldn't spend your life alone." "Maybe you're right John," I said. And he looked at me, took the pipe from his mouth, tapped it against an ashtray, and knew I wasn't about to do anything.

"Will you get some coal?" he said. I extracted myself from the low armchair, lifted the near-empty coal scuttle and walked out of the living room and into the kitchen to the door at the back of the house.

Outside it was winter: cold, wet and miserable as I'd said earlier and been corrected. "It's wet and it is cold alright, but I wouldn't add misery to it," he'd said.

The coal shed was at one side of a small, well-kept garden. John planted potatoes, and early cauliflowers, and he'd put down some parsley, thyme, the wonderful smell when I passed his house that reminded me of Christmas stuffing.

The bolt on the shed resisted being pulled across the old door, then freed up suddenly, startling a wide-eyed cat mooching at the bins.

I grappled in the dark for a spade and shovelled the knobbly pieces of coal, and as I did wondered, who did this during the day when he was alone?

I lifted the weight of blackness and walked out of the shed, bolting the stubborn door on the way. This should keep him for a day or two; he never lit fires until late afternoon. And then I'd call again.

"Put a few of bits on it," he said, watching closely as I did.

"Not too much, I'll be going to bed soon,"

His wife had passed away two years previously, an event that I thought would break him. He'd always said he'd be the one to go first.

"Mary and me, we were together for fifty-three years, two of them I courted her," he said as I put the coal tongs away.

Years seem to pass.

"I couldn't stay with Jane," I blurted. "It was too hard."

He picked up his pipe, stuffed down tobacco from a pouch he kept close.

"It just didn't work out, John," I said.

He lit a match from a large box and puffed, inhaled, blew smoke, stayed silent.

"Your father was a good man," he said finally, "don't forget him and your mother: they had happy days together, it will always be hard and that's the way."

And the fire burned now with the extra bits, and I sat closer, feeling the heat and we looked at the television and he wanted the sound turned up so as to hear the news and get the weather.

"More of the same tomorrow, John," I said.

"Well, it is winter," he said. "Will you put the guard on the fire?"

I did.

And then I left, him rising from the chair, seeing me to the door, ignoring my protests of staying where he was, him saying, yeah, and getting up slowly, making his way behind me and wishing me good luck.

"It's quiet, he said," looking out at the night. "Very quiet."

I am Still Grateful

Thomond Gill

For the smile and the gentle
Okay then. When?
For the soon, soon. Now?
For forever. I will be. And then?

The tears, the pain, and gain?
Experience. The feeling
that shook me, threw me in what?
Direction. The feeling.

You gave me questions
my world, and all in it.
For those, even without answers
I am. Still. Grateful.

Aunty Jo's Talent for Gardening
(For Jo, 1913 - 2006)

Clare Farrell

It's a wonder
I often used to think
how such truly gorgeous flowers
found strength
year on year
to emerge revived
smiling broadly
from that tiny patch of ground
in the back yard
of number twenty-seven.

Fed on fag ash, strong tea
and your fond
familiar footsteps
they came out willingly
as decades passed
(and much loved lives)
resilient like you
standing there – remembering –
tea gone cold
from the constant pleasure
of their company.

If I Could Have Taken Ten Photos...

Thomond Gill

I'd have shot the laughing girl in the ragged, still shiny, wheelchair
manoeuvring the crowded biscuit aisles in Supervalu
and blown her up so you could see her too-bright white eye,
Jaffa cakes. And dirty pink converse.

I'd have framed the feeling on the girl in the pinstripe suit's face
Walking along the busy sunny morning quays
And focused on the way in trees sunny green light lies
the secret to a happy universe

I'd have captured the confused look about the blonde pigtailed girl
Holding her fat sisters, hand that didn't hold back
And zoomed in on her crooked grey skirt and school tie,
Striped. Her shirt and innocence.

I'd have blurred the faces of those who hurried past
The dirty man who sat on Grafton St.
And in the foreground shown his black brown yellow feet
Blistered, unmoving as he rocked.

I'd have snapped the Chinese man who pushed a pram
And laughed and talked to his spiky-haired son
In a wideshot that showed the bank and the cars
And how empty that shadowy backstreet is.

I'd have a close-up of my roommate on the couch
Snuggled in a blanket 'cos she's sick
A *mise en scène* of toilet roll, Lemsip, blue blanket,
Remote control and Cornetto.

I'd have made a collage of the girl in the fluorescent orange boa
on the balcony at the party next door:
Mixed Media with a broken speaker, an alarm clock
showing 5.30 a.m. Monday morning. And slept for a while.

the last three I would have taken of you…

that look on your face as you concentrated to undo my
necklace as you lay on me with no shirt on.
The way your long eyelashes lay on your cheeks as you slept
And how your eyes lit up when you saw me

But I will not photograph your soul. I want it for myself.

Shelter

Conor Ferguson

Howling wind. Pelting rain. Streetlight gathering dimly in a bus shelter. Windows weathered opaque. Inside, shadows ooze into people. He sits down. Somebody coughs. A puff of breath from someone else. Her. Eyes flicker, gleaming pinpricks, then look towards feet swallowed by the ground. She shuffles on her seat, silk skirt ruffling like a sweetie-bag. He smiles and so does she. And some shivery, lonely, candle-lit, lost little spark flares up between them. Like a touch, but warmer still. Like a light approaching. Then a shriek of brakes and her bus appears. She nibbles her tongue, and she goes.

Watching

Conor Ferguson

She is the most beautiful creature I have ever seen. Her skin looks so soft. Her face a tapering oval of perfection. She could probably be a model. But why would she want to be the centre of attention for drooling idiots? There's more to her than that. She's funny, I bet. And brainy too. The glare from the TV lights her graceful figure, as she moves around doing I don't know what. It's funny how TVs give off that strange blue glow. You can't see it when you're there, inside. Only when you are outside looking in.

The 21st Chromosome

Jody Ellen Collins

I don't like kids. I'll just come out and say it – I don't like them. I know how that sounds but I just don't like the way they always have runny noses or the way they are always sticky from something. The relentless whining, constant demands; there is nothing good about that. I don't even like the way most of them look after a certain age. Sure, zero to nine months, they all look like pictures on a calendar, if they are fat enough. At that period of time, they are something else, big eyes, smiling at nothing, grabbing instinctively at dogs and other animals that come into their range of view. I always found that bond pretty fascinating, how the little, little babies are drawn automatically to animals as if they still share the innate link to nature until it gets diluted by language and counting and finally forced out by cartoons and TV ads. But after that, when they start talking and their teeth start growing in like kernels on a bad ear of corn, that's when I go off them completely. I don't have a maternal instinct either, no biological clock ticking, not one surge of last-ditch effort hormones boiling up in my thyroid or wherever. Nothing. So I don't know exactly what paralysed me behind this little girl, this little girl with Down's Syndrome, who was in front of me in line at the Chinese food place, squinting up at the numbered menus on the wall. Her eyeglasses were thick and they made her eyes look small and the glint of the track lights on them was painful.

She wanted General Gau's Chicken, number 34. It comes with a choice of an egg roll or soup. She wanted the egg roll. I knew that because when she went to the counter she said it and yes her voice was low and her speech sounded like the words were pushed through Jell-O but I understood it, clearly, as if it were rain. But I couldn't breathe. I couldn't even move my body. I felt as if I were just hanging off the edge of a mountain for that single timeless, motionless second before the Fall. She wanted General Gau's Chicken Dinner and I knew it but the faces, those faces behind the counter, also suspended in my moment of an inhaled breath, they looked back and I knew they wouldn't make it easy.

"What's that?" they asked her sharply. They have accents that are hard to understand too and I thought that maybe they would be more forgiving of her vowel-heavy words. I wanted to say something. I could have stepped in at that point but her face was determined and calm and it kept me frozen. Either that or I just didn't know what to say or how to be. I am always such a phony when it comes to doing anything like taking authority, making things better. I have to think how someone else whom I admire for it, my mother or some character in a book would do it and then pretend I'm her. It's a terrible feeling, to not like children or even know how to be with them and it's not something I admit on a daily basis. The public outrage that follows such a woman, especially one that can still bear children, is medieval. I may as well walk through the town square naked and announce that I am a witch. At work – I work in an office – there are always instances of babies coming and a celebratory lunch for every phase. I'm pregnant. Tom and I are so pleased. And I go to all the lunches and the showers and I sign the cards that go to the hospital rooms and the eight pounds four ounces healthy babies that come home from them. And I wait for it to make sense to me.

Would this girl be considered healthy? I look at her body. She is stocky with thick legs and straight hair cut in a tidy way around her face. She has freckles and a pretty mouth that is forming the word 'General' for a second time. She wouldn't be considered 'normal', I am certain of that and I don't know a lot about these types of things. But I when I think of a normal kid, I think of one that wanders the neighbourhood in search of frogs with a stick in one hand and a net in the other. I think of normal kids as ones with skinned knees who play games in the street until the street lights come on but I don't see those kids anymore. I see ones that don't talk to strangers, are imprisoned in their houses by the threat of molesters, murders and pollen allergies. I see ones that fall in line without imagination, without courage. What if I have one of these children? What if I don't like my own children?

The girl asks again for her food and this time she says the number that goes with it. More puzzled faces. Again she says it, steady, without frustration, as if she would say it all day. One of the girls behind the counter finally understands and starts speaking to the others in Chinese, then there is a flurry of activity in the kitchen and the girl stands off to the side to wait. I manage to put in my order, although I don't feel hungry anymore, and I too, stand to the side to wait to be served. I feel like she and I have just won a battle, won a blue ribbon – something. I am almost exhausted by her effort. She is unaffected and watches the cars battle for position on Beacon Street at rush hour. I watch the cars too and I am not sure why I am there. For Chinese food that I don't want? I have felt like this for a while now and I think my boyfriend has felt it too. Last week he asked me to marry him. It wasn't really a proposal. One night after the movie we had just watched about some family who were going to make it after all, he said: "Maybe we should think about getting married." It wasn't really a proposal; it was more like a suggestion.

"Chris, My God. I thought you didn't like the idea?"

"I don't. I didn't. I just think maybe it's the right thing to do."

"What for?"

"Well, we might want to have a family some day."

I have to tell you, I felt a little betrayed. I thought we were in this together. I thought he was like me and didn't want to risk not being sure. I have had little daydreams about marrying him ever since that night but they always have some kind of dark spot, like occlusion in a diamond. Chris and I are married and we have all the nice things that married couples have. We have each other and that is good but there I am, pregnant for the first time, and I realize, even more than I do now, that I really don't like kids. Or worse, there I am, in a couple of years, pregnant for the first time and I am down on my knees praying for ten fingers, ten toes, a good heart. There I am praying for health and genetic balance of the 21st chromosome so no-one could tell me that I waited too long, that I made a mistake. But he is right to want to try. Everything does seem to be sort of pointless at a certain stage. Even my own body – here I am hauling around these big boobs, these hips, suffering monthly for an event that is never going to happen.

When they put the plate of steaming rice and chicken on the table, the girl begins to search in a white patent leather pocketbook she has tucked under her arm. I wonder who bought these for her. Did her mother take her to the store and pick it out for her? Did she buy her a soda and tell her how to use it? Did they have a nice day out when she was given that purse? I hope it is the way I have imagined it – I mean, it is really important for me that this is how she got this purse. For some reason that I don't understand, I need to know that she is happy and that things are OK for her… that she is content with her days. I am craving a sign of a smile – any acknowledgement of her triumphs at the food counter but there is more to be done and once again I find myself waiting on my breaths. She hasn't forgotten either. From the white bag, she pulls a matching change purse. The cashier has told her the cost of her food but she seems to know without him telling her. She pulls three dollar bills from the pocket and smoothes them out on the counter. The cashier doesn't make a move towards them and I am so grateful for that. Instead, he watches her progress in silence as I do. She pulls out a quarter and lays it on the counter. One dime, another and then another goes towards the collection. One nickel and two pennies... she pushes the bills and then the coins, one at a time, flat with her fingertips on their centers, towards the man. He swoops them off the edge of the table, they disappear into his hand and then they rejoin the common coinage in the till, never realising their significance.

She takes her food and sits at one of the little speckled tables. Finally she smiles, not for any other reason than the honeyed lumps of chicken in tangy sauce is very good this particular day. Maybe it is her favorite. Her focus on her food has closed me out of her experience. I am just one of the others in the restaurant who are more concerned with getting the driver back out on the road with several Pu Pu Platters for Two than with this little girl. Other children pass by the window, varying in age. Many ride bikes and all wear helmets. They ride behind their parents. They drink fruit juice and have healthy snacks in little Ziploc bags. There are some in minivans on their way to soccer practices or play dates. The older ones are tuned into music and say all the catch phrases to identify them as worthy of their peers. There are no ponds anymore, I suppose, no more frogs or trees to climb, so they go to dance and *tae kwon do*. When they get older they go to the Mall. I see the ones pass by that are slipping away as well, slipping to places where no one can reach them, where they become engulfed in anger or bitterness, or just rib-crushing emptiness.

There I am, married and pregnant, on my knees, praying that my unborn child can order Chinese Food without fear and be truly happy spooning it into her mouth. I pray for knowing when to buy a purse and knowing what to say when I explain it. I pray for frogs and for guidance. I don't pray for balance on the 21st chromosome. I don't care about it at all.

If I could, I would sit down with the girl and ask her why she likes that dish, what other things she likes; what makes her glad, maybe I could get them for her. But she doesn't need me. That's the problem with kids... they break your heart.

all
good things
begin

at home

Power Shower

Eobhan O'Brien

My temper is Victoria Falls this evening
Hitting you at high velocity.
I want you bowed low
But you just switch channel
And refer to the TV guide.

I'm chopping parsley and –
See this knife?
Sometimes I think I'm capable
Of dangerous acts.
Dinner on our knees
Watching the soaps
The glamorous life is ours.
Tonight, we'll go to bed.

Party Tricks

Marcella Morgan

I can see her now.

      She is in the centre of my aunt's living room

My mother
Bent from the hip
Face to the floor
           Her arms flung wide like wings
With index fingers pointed
           Faithful legs support her madness

She strains further does my mother
         She strains and her body
             Allows her to go as far as she wishes

She wishes to feel the edge of the cardboard box between her teeth

That would mean she's won the game.

Marina and the Green Man

Deborah Ballard

Marina was born in the middle of the Black Winter, when the beasts froze in the fields and coals were rationed. Her parents set her cot in the kitchen, near the only fire, but still the night-light would be frozen in its saucer by morning, and the window-panes blind with ice. Her little body survived that savage cold unharmed, but all her life her spirit would fail at the coming of winter.

As Christmas approached, and her brothers and sisters went wild with excitement, Marina retreated into her books, opening the door to the Secret Garden with Mary and Dickon, or trembling as Blind Pew tapped remorselessly closer. Her mother wondered a little, and encouraged her to help make the cakes and puddings and hang up paper chains. And of course Marina did love Christmas, the presents, and Baby Jesus in the manger, and granny and the uncles sitting down to dinner with them, and especially, before anyone else was awake, pulling the crackly stocking from the bottom of the bed, and trying to guess what was in it. But even before the tree was taken down and the thank-you letters written, Marina grew quiet and inward again, until Spring, when she ran as wild and bold as any other child.

Shortly before her sixteenth birthday her father died, and when she left home her horror of the dark days grew worse. Her spirits sank each December, not so badly that she could not hand in her essays, but enough to make her avoid the other students, even her friends. She would walk home along Grafton Street among the determined shoppers, and as she looked at the fairy-tale puppets in Brown Thomas' windows she felt as if she too were going through the motions of being human.

By the time she was twenty-five, Marina thought she should do something about her annual purgatory. "A lot of people get depressed around the time of their birthdays," her therapist said. "It marks another year in which you may have failed to achieve what you hoped for." Marina thought this might well be true, but found it rather discouraging. That year she spent Christmas in Australia with her sister Katie, and came home in high spirits. "It doesn't mean it was the long sunny days," said her therapist. "You probably felt better because you didn't have the usual responsibilities of your job or relationships." Although he helped her understand her depressions, Marina realised that they were not going to go away. At first she would try to go somewhere hot over New Year, but later she preferred to stay at home, devising ways of reducing her workload, and folding herself away for the winter like linen. She had learned to live with her depressions; they were part of her, and besides, if she refused to submit to them, who knew what horrible thing might rear up to take their place?

Marina's husband Ally now accepted that she needed to withdraw from the world at Christmas time. He bought most of the presents and sent off the cards, and cheerfully went off to spend Christmas Day with his family, leaving his glum wife at home. He had at first tried to encourage her to join in the festivities, with her family or his, or even by themselves, but he soon realised how hard it was for her; nor did her presence contribute to the general joy. Marina would spend Christmas Day alone at home in front of the fire, nibbling figs and walnuts, and drinking wine. She felt relief knowing that no one would call, that she need not answer the phone, that even her amenable husband would not be coming back until Stephen's Day.

One year it began to snow on Christmas morning, and Marina began to fear that Ally would not be able to drive down to his parents' house at the other end of the county. She was appalled at how savage she felt about the threat to her precious solitude. Yet she loved her husband dearly, and she had been touched, when they exchanged gifts over breakfast in bed, to see that he had bought her something she'd seen and thought she could not afford: an old edition of Sir Gawain and the Green Knight, bound in rusty leather. She pulled herself together and resolved to be a better wife.

She was reluctantly pulling on her clothes, wondering what could she find in the freezer to make a Christmas dinner, when Ally came back into the room. "I've checked the weather forecast," he said, "And it's not going to be too bad. The main road will be open, all right. I'll get off now, before it gets any worse."

"Are you sure, Ally? You'll ring me as soon as you get there?"

"I will of course. Now, why don't you come into the sitting-room? I've made a fire and set a bottle of wine to breathe. Is there anything else you'd like before I go?"

The room was lit by the leaping fire and the tiny lights threading the holly he'd hung on the walls. A bowl of fruit, a nutcracker and one of the good glasses stood on the sofa-table. Tears came to her eyes as she thought of his kindness, but as she settled in before the fire with her marvellous book, she hugged her solitude to herself, and quietly unfolded in the warmth.

Childlike, she looked at the pictures in Sir Gawain before starting on the text. Here was Arthur keeping Christmas with his court, feasting, singing and telling tales, but outside the wolves howled, and Marina felt the fear behind the feasting: Will we live through the winter? And then came the knock on the door, and in rode Fear made manifest, the Green Knight, gnarled and vigorous as a winter holly, shouting out his challenge and making his wicked bargain with Gawain.

Gawain looked very young and beautiful in the pictures, and his red horse was more elegant than the Green Knight's green one. Marina began to read, quickly losing herself in the story. Startled by the telephone, she remembered Ally, and jumped up to answer it.

"I've made it, sweetheart." His voice, so reassuring. "It was bad enough at Rathnew, but the lane here's still open. There was hardly anyone on the roads, though. We're just sitting down to dinner.

– How are you doing, Marina?"

"I'm grand, Ally. It's snowing quite hard here, too. Oh!" She was startled by the lights going out. "No, it's nothing, Ally, just a bulb gone. Enjoy your dinner, and wish them all a very happy Christmas from me." But as she knew, the electricity had failed, and with the weather like this it might be off for a while.

She felt sorry for the families still cooking the turkey, trying to find candles and get a fire going. She looked out, and where before distant houses had blazed with lights, she could hardly see her neighbours' roofs between the trees. Snow continued to fall, and the wind was rising. She brought in more logs, lit some candles and settled into the sofa with her book.

Gawain was lost in the frozen waste, despairing of finding the Green Knight's castle, when Marina decided it was time for a treat. She fetched her little brass box and started rolling herself a joint. Ally didn't like her smoking, and Marina knew he was right, that it didn't help when her spirits were low. But that was when she loved it most, the way it made her senses come alive again for a time. It's good stuff all right, she thought, finding herself entranced for several minutes by the picture of Gawain on his red horse. The cat came in and jumped up beside her. "Tadhg! Tadhg!" she crooned, "Mammy's tiger-boy! You like it when I'm stoned, don't you?"

Marina was enchanted by Tadhg's dense winter coat under her fingers, the wind crying in the chimney, the low gleam of firelight on the swags of holly. Thirsty, she ate a pear, giggling as the juice ran down her chin. But then she began to shiver uncontrollably, and realised that she'd smoked too much. The cat stared at her, twitching his tail, as she crouched close to the fire.

There was an appalling crash in the kitchen and Tadhg shot under the sofa. Marina saw the fire flare in the icy wind, and looked up to see great branches of holly thrusting through the wall towards her. The Green Man had burst into her fastness, a demonic presence before which she sprawled in terror and wonder. She had tried to shut out the wild things, but they were not to be denied, and even as her heart hammered with fear, she admired the savage energy of this being, which flourished in the dark and cold that shrivelled her spirit.

She forced herself to look into the creature's face, and the gnarled features tamely resolved into the holly Ally had hung on the wall. She cautiously got to her feet and shut the back door. The wind was driving the snow before it, and it was bitterly cold. As she bolted the door, properly this time, Tadhg reappeared from under the sofa, and she picked him up to comfort him. "Scary stuff, Tadhg, but we'll be safe and warm tonight, you and I." She relit the candles and settled back into the sofa with a brandy. As warmth returned, she thought of the sun which had fattened the grapes and which blazed in her grate, released from long sleep in tree and log; summer did not seem quite so far away.

Later that evening the lights came back on, but Marina turned them off, preferring the simplicity of candlelight. She slept very well that night, with Tadhg allowed onto the bed for once, and Gawain had returned from his quest, shame-faced but wiser, before she blew out her candle. She fell asleep thinking about Gawain's bravery and his one moment of cowardice, and wondered was the fear of death something you just had to learn to live with.

Early next morning the wind had dropped, and Marina looked out on a frozen snowscape shrouded in fog. But there was a radiance in the east which suggested a brighter day, and she got up at once instead of going back to bed with a pot of tea. She pulled on her warmest clothes, put a lock-knife in her pocket and started walking up the glen towards the woods. It was still not broad day, but she knew the way and was soon at the forest edge. The frosty air was very still and her senses seemed sharpened; she could hear a robin somewhere, and twigs snapped sharply under her boots. She passed between the trees until she found what she was looking for: a great holly, thirty feet tall, flush and potent among its leafless companions. "I want a piece of you, Green Fella," she said, and took out her knife and cut as many branches as she could carry.

As she returned through the trees she felt them instinct with life in their winter sleep, and touched their bark as if to feel the slow sap beneath. She added long stems of ivy to her armful of holly, and some hazel branches hung with catkins, delighting in this token of spring. Nearing home, she met a neighbour walking his dogs and stopped a moment to exchange greetings.

"Won't you and Ally call in and see us over the Christmas, Marina?" he said, and to her surprise, she found herself promising that she would.

Ally could not get home until the following day. He was surprised to see a holly wreath nailed to the front door, but when his smiling wife opened it, he was speechless. Ivy wound thickly round the banisters, bound with scarlet ribbon, and every wall was festooned with holly. Branches of bay and rosemary filled the house with their spiciness, and there were jam-jars stuffed with hazel-twigs on the windowsills. Delicious smells were coming from the kitchen, an extravagant fire blazed in the sitting room, and Marina had spread the big table with a linen cloth and the best delph for what looked to be a splendid dinner. Tears filled his eyes, and he hugged her very tight, feeling her wriggle delightedly in his arms, like a child who's made a wonderful surprise, as of course she had.

Marina never completely lost heart, in winter, after that. Although friends and family went down to death, her fear of it gave way to small daily pleasures and doing the best she could. Every year she brought in holly and ivy from the woods, filled the house with light and warmth and cooked a midwinter feast for Ally and their friends – fat goose, puddings stuffed with raisins and currants, and wine grown rich under a long summer's sun. And every winter she read Sir Gawain to remind herself that living bravely is the best riposte to death.

The Secret Life Of My Mum

Clare Farrell

On Mondays when we're at school my mum runs a Jedi academy
Teaching defensive and offensive light sabre techniques
In our front room
To budding Jedi apprentices who land in their fighter ships
On the runway in the back garden
And if anyone calls during training she has to pretend
Not to be at home.

On Tuesdays when we're at school she holds secret meetings
Of the Republican Senate plotting against the dark side
With the blinds drawn
Tracing dotted lines through great maps of the galaxy spread
Out across the kitchen table
And if my dad phones she answers nonchalantly while the senators
Try to keep the noise down.

On Wednesdays when we're at school she works alone on research
Crucial to the enhancement of battle droid features
In the quiet of our study
Slowly marking out improvements on the detailed drawings
Yoda's sent that morning
And then hides them in a secret drawer she thinks I haven't seen
Before its time for lunch.

On Thursdays when we're at school she takes off on a classified mission
To counsel Tusken Raiders against savage undertakings
Coming home a little shaken but
Carefully guiding her jet into a deep recess at the back of our shed
Without the neighbours knowing
And then acts as if she's had an easy day listening to Joe
And making shepherd's pie.

On Fridays, I haven't figured out her duties
I'm still sifting through the clues
So maybe I'll develop a headache
And stay at home from school
Because I'm inches away from being certain
My mum's a Jedi, cool!

Silence in Darkness

C.M. Rice

1.02 a.m. and he creaks up the stairs – no-one awakens, only an alarm clock beeps from a door down the hall. His door sounds in kind with the stairs to add to the silence he hears in darkness.

A red-orange glow meets his eye: not enough to show the way. He stops, transfixed by the warmth of familiarity: a beautiful second he feels before the insistant artificial light stares out from a forgotten corner.

A half-eaten apple – yellow – chooses its moment to fall and roll towards him; he steps over it and it resigns itelf and rests with the post which lies jumbled by the door ajar. The second passes, and he thinks: if only it could last so as not to have to flick on the light, yet as the hope of calming air is lost this light brightens the room whole. He closes the door with a push of post and a kick of apple into this contemptuous shell.

He shuffles to the only seat in sight, an armchair. He slumps, dust rises and he sighs instinctively. He always does this: a most unfortunate habit. Rubbing his weary eyes, light spears through. It annoys his face, rough with reality from the night just gone. He notices through pure frustration and discomfort that his once impeccable coffee table, important as he bought it for himself all by himself, sits strewn with tobacco and ash. He could clean it and it would jump out again to greet his aching feet and legs, but no, it lays untidy like the jacket he still wears.

The clock is finally heard as the embers in the fireplace scowl at the night above. The embers have company though, as his stomach grumbles. Food. Not dinner, as dinner is prepared with consideration for what it is and whom it is for. Food is what is there: no consideration necessary.

So, under pressure from the gripes and moans of stomach and hearth (particles of dust invading an already sensitive nose cold from the outside) he concedes, wrapping his jacket around him cocooning the recent warmth, that he will make or find food.

Another habit kicks in, as he ponders what remains on the counter to eat. He questions why he had not reached sooner, as they were sticking into his hip in his tight jeans stuck with rain: a smoke. His red-numb hands, with fingers yellow as the ignored apple, search. He inhales sharply the stagnant air which catches his throat as he lunges upwards needing a proper smoke: mass-produced, perfectly rolled, with an impresive and inviting filter. He sighs again – why should he bother? It is never a good sign when one's only friend has the possibility of burning down and completely out, and anyway, his cigarette box is swimming in a pocketful of wet coins and tissues.

Food would provide his satisfaction. Bread is the highlight of the evening. It is smelled and the butter avoided; it seems peculiarly bright. His black Parka jacket drips like a leaky tap, creating two small puddles on old cream lino floor.

"Tomorrow's sun will dry that up," he thinks, struggling with barely enough will to chew this bread which sits like a wet ball of playdoh on his dry palate; maybe the shiny butter could have helped. He coughs this sphere of yeast and flour into his surprised hands and sighs once more. Water.

He trips lazily as he approaches the tower of dishes with its moat of stale suds in a sink marked dirty like the inside of a favourite cup. Not finding a glass, he chooses to scoop water into his face, hoping this clears the empty lump sitting on his wheezy chest. He swallows uncomfortably. Choking a little as he sees the colour run from clear to misty, holding himself up with two shaking forearms his head thumps out of time with the clock now showing 1.07 a.m.

Sudden movements from next-door startle him. He tries to listen for voices but hears only "tick – thump – tock – thump – drip – drip," loud and concentrated as if those noises were sitting on his ear drums. He closes his weary eyelids seeing only white bright stars happily moving to the unpleasant rhythm. Even with a swift opening of his eyes he sees them too – they mock his dire mood. His state worsens as he turns sharply, trying to shake off those eye dancers. Wishing now only for sleep, yet knowing he can barely move, leaves him stranded. Wiping away the murky water with a damp sleeve he stands alone.

Time to switch out this light and stay captive in the company of the silence in darkness.

Frankie is Queen

Jenny Wright

The girls had to be very good and if they were, they could come down and see Mum and Dad before they went out. Lizzie was looking after them and they didn't like her because she scrubbed their faces with the cloth too hard. She did it on purpose. They usually complained, but this time, because Mum and Dad were going out to a ball, the girls were too excited and couldn't wait to get downstairs to see them. Jo was wearing her boy's pyjamas, cotton stripes with a rope cord and a slit for her willie which hadn't yet grown. No matter how often she stood up to pee, no willie appeared. Boys had a better deal, they were more important than silly girls and they were allowed to do things girls weren't.

Faces scrubbed red and teeth scraped white, curly hair unknotted, they raced down into the warm sitting room. Mum was in a long white dress with no straps. "How does it stay up?" "Oh look it's got bones." She was wearing bright red lipstick and looked so different that Jo couldn't really look at her straight. She liked Mum's tweed skirt better and the rough cardigan with the pockets full of dog biscuits. Dad was leaning on the mantlepiece with a glass of smelly brown stuff in his hand and looking really uncomfortable with a bow tie strangling him. His neck was a bit bulgy and he was twisting his head round and pulling at the tie. They looked so posh. The girls couldn't speak: Mum and Dad were weird.

Dad turned to the girls and asked them how to get out of dancing with Mum and Mum said, "Oh, never mind, Johnny will dance with me."

Mum swished as she walked and smelled funny when she bent over to kiss them goodnight, with her usual, "Be good."

Jo woke up with the clink of ice in glasses and the skoosh of tonic being opened from the drink cupboard on the downstairs landing. She got out of bed and crept down to the sitting room and opened the door. Dad and a man with exactly the same clothes as Dad were sitting on the window seat talking in rumbling voices and smoking. Mum and the Queen were standing on either side of the fireplace, each holding a glass with steam on the outside and ice inside and lemon. The Queen had a long red dress made of shiny stuff. She smiled. Mum smiled and said in a voice that sounded far away and not the same as usual, "Hello darling", which she never called her, "What are you doing up so late?"

Dad came over and was holding Jo's hand when she knew she had to curtsy to the Queen. She tried to say something, but nothing seemed right. What do you say to a Queen in the middle of the night? Dad told her to say goodnight and it was time to go back to bed. Jo saw they were all smiling in that way that made her feel small and silly and want to hit them.

At breakfast, Jo kind of knew it wasn't the Queen. She had to ask in a casual voice, but they did that smiling thing again and told her it was only Frankie Ives. After a bit they agreed that Frankie did look quite like the Queen, but Jo stamped off, saying that she had only been joking anyway. Her big sister told her she should have known it wasn't the Queen because she didn't wave, only smiled. But Jo only wished she'd remembered to bow instead of curtsy.

That Room

Samantha McCaffrey

Everything happened in rooms. It seems sometimes to be the one room, the same one, again and again. Our father's house had many rooms. Each one had a door that locks itself from the inside. Each one reminds me of you and me.

Your bedroom is called the box room. A small square room, ice-white cold. Tonight, like other nights, it's the boxing room where you get your ears boxed off you. Again and again. The door is open and its steel handle watches it all happen silently. You scream each time that our dad whips you with his black leather belt. No wonder you piss your bed every night. I do too and I'm only watching. I can see it happen in double, right in front of my eyes our father is clenched and you are skinnier than a twig. I see it mirrored in your bedroom window a second time while I watch. I am frozen, the little ice queen, cracking slowly on the inside. Dad is topless. He is only wearing his faded blue jeans, like Starsky or Hutch would, his arms taut. He is still beautiful to me. I know it's hurting him but he still does it. On and on he lashes you while you scream. Your room has become the ice room with its white walls. Vacant walls peppered only with Dad's handprints, little bruises where he tried to pin you down.

The kitchen is the sick room. Faded pink walls with bright orange tiles, cracked and browning like a heart. We sit there, you and me, with our sick little sister. Our mother has gone. It seems she can't take it. All the doors are closed and the open kettle boils on and on. One of us must refill it. The kettle coughs, like our sister who is flagging in her big brown pram. Her white terry-cloth sheet holds her damp stain like a warm hand. You and I don't look at each other or talk. All we can do is sit and stare. I am worried our little sister is going to die, but still I sit. The steam suckers us onto the fake leather cushions of the kitchen chairs. The steam hazes out the glare of the sick orange tiles. The small television left on the counter to keep us occupied has turned all the people's faces orange instead.

Drops form on the kitchen window waiting to rain-wash our room, watermarks not big enough to cry. I wish my mum would come back. Hours seem to pass and she does not. I've no idea what you're wishing, jerking and flailing on your chair. The rows of drops gather and grow like a row of faces, or suburban houses, empty, no one home. I can't breathe now. I can't see you and it's not just the mist in the kitchen. We always found it hard to see each other, our eyes lost to ourselves like our mother's dreams. The steam drops build with too many moments crowding the air. We gulp it back down till we are drowning in our own swallowings. On our outside, our eyes twitch; I have a nervous knee and you a nose-picking finger. Inside, we are treading our own waters. The wooden table sits dead by the wall. Everything has been left.

This today is like every day. This room like all the others. At night we sleepwalk, intoxicated by the smell of our own piss. We walk from room to room, feeling the walls for a mother or father hiding behind them. By day, we hunt for warmth, missing each other on our separate routes.

Another room. Another boxing ring. This time in the sitting room where I crawl under the couch and you watch too much TV. Then, there is a new dog. New and warm, we both want to eat him alive. He is full of life but he will change. He will become flat-headed, scared. He will learn, like we have, that you can't be with someone and against them at the same time.

"He loves me more." You are playing with the dog, bobbing a yo-yo, higher and higher to make him walk.

"Wanna bet?" I shout back into your face.

This is the beginning of a game we play often. It will end in fighting and biting. I will pull your hair from the top of your purple face. You will thump me in the belly till I howl out. Both of us will feel warm after in a numb way. Today ends slightly differently because the new dog is here.

Your walk is determined. The dog is placed in the middle of the room. We both walk to the corners of the room and face each other.

"Go." You scream as you begin to call the dog. You start out standing, your arms waving. Me too. You call the dog. I call the dog. We start soft but that doesn't last long. You stamp and I dance. I twist and you turn. Each corkscrew turn urges our mouths to open wider.

"Come here." You have your hands out.

"Come here." Louder, I have started to bang the floor.

"This way." You're on the floor now, begging.

"No. No. No." I bang the floor with each word.

"Come fuckin, here." You're crawling and wriggling.

"Don't listen to him." I bare my teeth.

"Come here. NOWW." Your tongue points out.

Then come the serious voices with tones stolen from adults. Next, open screams, moon-sized. And the dog is just dizzy in the middle of the floor.

Our mouths open wider; ugly raw lipped while the dog yelps running this way and that. We can just barely hear the rip of his little throat sounds, a sliced heart, beyond our screams. We are at home watching the dog run in circles surrounded by cries. We have taught him well. When you're half-finished and broken-eyed, you know it. Now the dog did too.

Our mother has gone for good. Dad's room has turned into the rotting room. The rain gets in through the warped wood around the window. The cream backing on the wine curtains has greened. Dad won't move. He just rots. He never washes and he won't throw anything out. He lines up his collection of shoes all around the walls of his bedroom. He powders them with talcum and the insoles just go green too. The talcum doesn't hide the smell of his rot but add to the marbled mix of hunger and hatred and bad breath. I live in fear of seeing his feet. He locks his room to keep his secrets and his smells to himself. Even with the door locked the smell seeps out and gnaws at you and me. I am scared it will eat you and me. The belly of his bed is gouged out from his sweat, tufts of fibres trying to escape. The middle of the mattress is a big holed mouth that is eating any sad smiles he had left. I hate it when Dad takes our little sister to that bed with him. I worry that the mouth will swallow her. The rotting room with the rotten bed and bad mouth smells. We are all hungry.

There are these rooms. There are more rooms. One for each memory. In some way, they are all the same. I can't remember them all. I can remember empty rooms too. You say you remember nothing. And then you say nothing. We never talk about the rooms, you and me.

Forty Good Years

Lori Johnston

He still does the crossword in The Guardian every day, but he can't be left to make his own breakfast. He will argue on politics and philosophy with me until the wee hours, and yet I'll wake in the night to find the mattress beside me cold and empty, while he wanders the house bleating like a lost child. He reads my work and writes shrewd and biting comments in the margins, and yesterday he slipped out while I was in the bathroom, and walked to the post office in his pyjamas.

To begin with it was tiny lapses that were barely noticeable, the sort of thing we all do. He'd lose his keys or a paper he was working on, or forget a meeting with a colleague. Keys would show up in the pockets of jackets and papers would show up sheaved between the leaves of a reference he'd been using. Crusty academic colleagues often neglected to notice his absence anyway, absorbed as they were in their own work.

It grows worse only gradually, punctuated with the occasional drama that terrifies me, and makes me think of what it will be like weeks and months down the line. At the very beginning, I used to leave him alone when I went to teach a class, making sure he had breakfast and rushing back at lunchtime so that he wouldn't have to try doing anything for himself. It was hopeless of course, something was bound to happen sooner or later. I returned one lunchtime, wearily hoisting my briefcase and a paper carrier of textbooks against me as I struggled to unlock the back door. My bones ached and I wanted nothing more than a cup of tea and some time to gather my strength in peace. At times like this I wondered why I carried on tutoring, thought about giving up and retiring into peaceful old age. My clumsy fingers finally managed to turn the key in the lock, and as I pushed the door wide the smell of gas hit me. I froze, hand halfway to the light switch. Then I dropped my books with a cry and ran to the cooker, twisting knobs and flinging open the window.

Afterwards, as I stood slumped against the cooker, hand clutched to my forehead and imaging so many more scenarios, he ambled into the kitchen. He smiled and came forward to kiss my cheek.

"Had a good morning, love?" he asked affably. Then, sniffing the air, "Did you leave the gas on?"

After that I knew I couldn't leave him alone any more. I try to organise for one of the children or a friend to drop by and sit with him where I can, but I had to cut back on my classes. I'd go out of my mind at home all day, with nothing to do, but for now I've got my book to keep me occupied. In the longer term, he'll probably need more hands-on care anyway.

I lie in the bath at night after he has gone to sleep. The warm moisture in the air makes my breathing feel laboured. The house is very quiet, with only the gurgling of water in the pipes and the lap of it against the sides of the bath when I move. I think about our lives together, and remember him how he was when we first met and courted, and all the years together since. This isn't how I imagined our old age together. He is getting worse, slipping further and further away. A bit of me is always scared now; scared when I leave him alone, in case something happens to him, and scared of what he is becoming and what I am losing.

I can't imagine how he must feel. He has lucid periods – long, long stretches when he seems fine. Then he'll be pottering away at something, and realise he has no idea what he is doing, or why; or if I am in the house, or if he has eaten, or fed the cat. He is losing his mind, but, paradoxically, he knows it. No, I can't imagine how frightened he must be. He once described it to me as being like a fog that he wanders in and out of. He can't remember where he's been, and though he's been there, he hasn't seen anything. Sometimes the fog thins to wisps, and other times it melts away to nothing. Other times, it comes down like a blanket, and smothers him.

I do get impatient. We have the same conversations over and over. He'll ask me a question, and five minutes later he'll ask me again. Sometimes, I snap at him. He looks hurt and bewildered. "I told you" I say, and he raises his eyebrows at me: "I don't remember." Occasionally, very occasionally, if I am busy, if I have my back to him when he asks for the third time, I will pretend I haven't heard, bustling out of the room muttering about seeing to the washing, or rustling the newspaper loudly. I feel guilty about that, and I know I'll cry about it when he's gone.

I shift in the bath. The water is growing colder and I think about the pile of papers that is waiting on my desk upstairs. I don't sleep so well now; it is often easier to work during the night, when he is asleep and there are no distractions. It stops me thinking about things.

Sighing, I heave myself out of the water and pull the plug; as the water gurgles away, I dry myself and pull on a towelling dressing gown. Everything seems an effort. I'm old too, I remind myself. My sad, sagging body knows it even if my mind doesn't.

I pause by the bedroom door and peer in. He is sleeping quietly. I hope he remains so. In the study I turn on the computer; pour a glass of wine and light a cigarette. Bad habits, but they haven't killed me yet. I begin to sort through the papers that lie in messy heaps on the desk, wondering where to begin. I flick idly through the marked-up manuscript of the book, grimacing at the petty editorial comments. More wine first I think.

I've been working for a couple of hours when the study door opens, and he comes in, smiling gently. I think for a moment that he has got lost on the way back from the bathroom, but looking into his eyes I realise he is in his right mind.

"Do you realise it is half-past-three in the morning?"

I nod, "Work to do."

"Can I get you a drink or anything?" he asks. "You shouldn't stay up too late. You'll tire yourself."

I smile at his concern.

"I must finish this."

"OK. But come to bed soon," he smiles, pats my hand, and makes to leave. I watch him go sadly. He isn't so often himself now.

"Wait," I call after him. "Put the kettle on, and I'll be down in a minute."

He turns in the doorway, "Don't get distracted and forget to come down then. I know what you're like. I'll give you five minutes."

I nod and watch as he closes the door, then I sigh and turn off the computer, bundling the manuscript together on the desk.

We had forty good years together, and there aren't many people who can say that. I switch off the lamp and follow him downstairs.

The Last Wolf Meets the Last Woman Whose Mother Tongue was Cornish

Deborah Ballard

I was hungry, that winter,
Leaving the frozen woods to pick
My way through the human world.
One night I followed you home.

You did not look, but you knew I was there,
Watching at the threshold.
You stirred the fire against the wintry air
That blew through the half-open door.

When the moon set, you took the lamp
And rose to go to bed.
I snatched a ham-bone from the table
And fled back to the woods.

Two nights later, I came back.
You seduced me with a dish of milk
Between your long silence and the door;
I came in to sit by your stool.

Now I lie on your bed,
My nose against your arm.
I bring rabbits and young deer,
To lay at your feet.

You took my wildness,
But you made me complete.
I am awkward still.
But I am learning to speak.

The Bedroom

Barry Brown

What say you to me Pope John Paul? What say you to Leonard James Martin? Not a word from you, hangin' over me bed and presidin' over the Room of Truth. And that'll do just fine. Now that you're here, I can relax and take things aisy. There's no voices goin' off in me head. That last bollocks, Padro Pio, was always at me to get at meself with the razorblades. He'd be wakin' me up in the middle of the night, screamin' orders at me.

"Martin ya no good bastard, do it now."

"Martin ya Rat. End it now and put us all out of our misery."

And I nearly did it as well. More than once if the truth be told. And expect nathin' less in the Room of Truth. Three times I had the blade out and was about to give these walls a coat of red to bate the band. And three times Jimi Hendrix and Phil Lynott saved me. Told me to chill out and be cool dudes like them.

So say I to you Pope John Paul, say I to you preside away over the Room of Truth. And don't worry, Lenny Martin's also watchin' your back. Soon as I save the sponds I'll get a flight over to Rome and bust ya out of the Vatican. We'll bate the shite out of that German impostor and before ya know it you'll be back on the throne again. That'll be some craic. Yeee-hawww!

What say you to me Phil Lynott? What say the King of the Jailbreaks to Lenny Martin? How many nights did we spend together, plottin' and plannin' me escape from the 'Joy? All good to go we were as well. I was just waitin' for the nod from yourself, and I would have busted out of that shithole. The bastards got wind though, and ripped down me poster. And no poster meant no more Phil Lynott and Lenny Martin in cahoots.

But fair play to ya Phil, ya tried to send messages via me song. And despite all the prison memories, its still me favourite.

'Tonight there's gonna be jailbreak, somewhere in this town'

"Tonight there's gonna be a jailbreak and Lenny Martin's hittin' town."

What make you, Phil Lynott, what make you of these two items I carry in me pocket? One sent, the other taken. Taken by a cunnin' opportunist at an opportune time. Fruits of sharin' a house with a very pretty lady. She's givin' me all the signs all right. What else was she doin' leavin' her sexy knickers in the hotpress? Sure sign. Sure fuckin' sign.

But first I have to deal with me other business. The letter sent from Kerry. Close the curtains. Don't want any nosey-poseys gawkin' in me window. I have to be careful pullin' them over, in case I knock over me fishin' rod. Its been a long time since I did a spot of fly-fishin'. Great whites are the problem. The last two times I was down by the Liffey I seen the big fin comin' for me, and fuckin' legged it.

Now I've made the Room of Truth private, I reach under the bed and pull out the ole' shoebox that I call me collection box. Mostly full of pictures and press-clippin's. But if ya want the lifestory of Lenny Martin, look no further. Goes all the way back to me primary school days.

There's a picture of me class that made the Confirmation. Some craic that was, me with the big black teeth from horsin' down gobstoppers. I can still put a name to all the other faces, even though I've stabbed out all the eyes. I had to do it. The Judas bastards have all betrayed me. And this letter from Kerry, is from the original Judas.

Hi Leonard
Thought I'd send this letter as you said you would be away for a while. No news from here – we are all just trying to keep warm and dry. Lousy weather.

Love, Mum

Shnivellin' bitch! Tryin' to spy on me again. But I'm onto her, I know her game. She had me life plagued from day one. George Martin said she had me spoiled and was makin' me soft. Buyin' me Tayhee's and Mars bars and TK Red Lemonade. And in those days George Martin was always right. Or so he believed.

Big George Martin, no longer the most important man in the bottom half of Newbridge. No longer Treasurer of Southfields GAA Club, best club in Newbridge. And no longer do the parishioners of the bottom half of Newbridge pay homage to the owner of the George's Grocery, best shop in Newbridge.

"What say you George, will this be our year?"

"What say you George, we will have a good run at the championship this year?"

Good questions. Fair questions. And relevant questions. We all knew the answer. Everyone in the bottom half of the town knew the answer.

Even Little Lenny Martin knew the answer. It was simple, bate Mountfield and it'd be a good year. Couldn't give a fiddlers about anythin' else, as long as we bate Mountfield.

But we had to hear it from Big George. The man in charge of the money. The man with his own business, big house and flashy car. The man with the best catch of a wife. Not only all the way from Kerry, but also brother of Tadhgie Fitzgerald, GAA legend and winner of six All-Ireland medals. Six more then were in the rest of Newbridge. In his position of authority, a nod of George's head was all that was needed.

But there were other questions.

"What make you George, what make you of the young lads comin' up the ranks?"

Not too bad on its own, but then they got always caught up in the Southfields Fever. Next thing there'd be a wink at me followed by the inevitable.

"What say you George, is there a bit of Fitzgerald in this fella?"

"What say you George, will this fella be as good as his Uncle?"

The Southfields Fever would often take a grip of me too. Every evenin' I'd be pesterin George.

"What say you Da, when'll you bring me to Southfields?"

"What make you Da, what make you of the medals I'll win? Won't I be like Uncle Tadghie?"

First time Little Lenny Martin was brought down to the Club, I couldn't wait. Me Ma had bought me a new Kerry jersey with the number 15 on the back. Uncle Tadghie's number.

They ran me 'till I puked me ring up. All the other big lads were laughin' their holes off at the Little Fat Kerry Bastard. Worse again, they refused to pass me the ball durin' trainin', but battered into me if it happened to be close by. I remember that day like it was yesterday, me covered in me own vomit and standin' around like a spare prick on the pitch. I was too scared to move, and Big George starin' at me with The Look from the sideline didn't help. I would have been a lot worse had I known what The Look meant.

I found out later that day. Once in the house, Big George blasted me an almighty kick up the hole. After all me bravado, I'd fuckin' shamed him and his Club by not even tryin'. He was just about to deliver another when me Ma came rushin' in from the kitchen. Ballin' her eyes out. The schnivellin' bitch tried to console me, but I just pushed her away and fucked off to me room. I was too sore and angry to cry, but at least I had the strength to rip her Kerry jersey to shreds. It was that and all her fuckin' Tayhee's, Mars and lemonade that were to blame.

I knew better then not to go back to Southfields the next Saturday. It wasn't so bad that week, and there was no batin' or ballin' when we got home. Being young and naive, I thought that was the end of that. I was wrong. I can't even remember what I did the second time to disgrace George and his Club, only that I pissed blood for a couple of days.

Nathin' I did was ever good enough. And fuckin' eejit that I was, I tried. Hoppin' ball, kickin' ball, scorin' ball. Look at me Da, look at me play. No doubt, all those batin's have toughened me up no end. Don't worry Da, I'll win the championship for Southfields. Don't worry Da, we'll bate Mountfield so you won't have to bate the shite out of me and there'll be no more ballin' from that no good Fitzgerald whore from Kerry.

And I didn't let ya down Da, didn't I not? Three county medals I won for your fuckin' club. And what say you? Fuck all, that's what say Big Fat George Martin who never kicked a ball in his life.

And what say you when we lose the county final to Mountfield? When I made a laughing stock out of George and his Club. Plenty to say that night, didn't ya? But ya never estimated how much fight would be in this seventeen year old. Lenny Martin was well able to handle Big Fat George Martin. What say you Da, when your only son bates the shite of ya?

And what say you Ma? You standin' there ballin' your fuckin' eyes out. Any excuse, sure ya even balled your eyes out when I did the big fancy Leaving Cert and got enough points to go to college. Like a fuckin' eejit ya got all worked up and started plannin' life for Leonard Martin, college student. Spendin' all your money on drivin' lessons so Leonard could come home at weekends.

What else did ya expect Lenny to do after batin' his Da? Course he fuckin' took the car out for a spin. But not your shitty little Fiat. Oh no, the new boss had to stamp his authority, and fuckin' quickly. Out he went in Big Fat George's Mercedes. Yee-hawww, crash, bang, screech and two fire brigades, three garda cars and an ambulance later they finally managed to separate the Mercedes, a big oak tree and Lenny Martin.

There were no more batin's from that day on. Half the problem solved. But there was plenty of fuckin' ballin'. Six weeks I spent in that fuckin' hospital with every sort of needle and tube shoved into me, and every time I woke up either one or the pair of them were standin' over me and ballin' their fuckin' eyes. And when me Ma wasn't cryin' she was talkin' shite about how I'd soon be right as rain, playin' ball and getting' ready for college.

George was sayin' fuckall. He'd caught a bad dose of the ballin' virus. I suppose he was always susceptible to it, bein' in close contact with me Ma, with his car bein' wrote off, havin' to take time away from the Shop and the Club, and no longer bein' able to bate his son. Plenty of reasons to ball his eyes out, and the root cause of all of them was one Lenny Martin. Yee-hawww!

What say you Lenny Martin? What say you to this visage reflected in the mirror before ya? What say you to the scars on your head? To the big dent in your forehead? Say I to you a fair trade. Once home there was no more talk of goin' to college, and no more havin' to play football for Southfields. Just me Ma waitin' on me hand over foot, and me Da tiptoein' around me.

The nurses told me that I was lucky not to have been killed. A lot of the time I disagree. I've done a lot of crazy things since that day. I look at me reflection in the mirror and know me face tells no lies. Compared to the picture of me confirmation, I've been heavily taxed. Its not just the scars. Its not just the crooked ears that give me the appearance that I've had me head wedged in a parking meter. Its more than that. Its the half-sneer me mouth seems to permanently have, coupled with the squinty eyes. Hold on, no secrets in Room of Truth. They're not just squinty eyes, they're squinty vermin eyes. Rat's eyes. That's what I've become. A Rat. Nathin' but a fuckin' Rat!

I'm well down the Rat Path now, and I know there's no goin' back. I've met a lot bigger and worse Rats on the way. But it was them who pushed me in that direction. Pauline's ballin's and George's batin's. And all those Judas's from school and from Southfields. Visitin' me in the hospital and pretendin' like they cared. But they didn't come often, and left mumblin' excuses about headin' away to college. But I know it was nathin' to do with that. Once the doctors removed all the tubes and bandages, they got to see what I was really like.

What say you Jimi Hendrix? What say you to Lobotomy Lenny? What say you to the 'Voodoo Child?'

I'm breathin' very heavily now, cause I know I'm beginnin' the Purification Ritual. I take out the big old safety pin from me bedside locker. I set it on top of the taken knickers and start to unbutton me jeans. Time to be the Voodoo Child.

Afterwards I don't even bother tryin' to find a dry part of her knickers to wipe down me cuts. The salt will make a good antiseptic.

I know this is wrong. But it helps. I have to carry on. We all do. Keep hard at it, and maybe, just maybe things will turn around and come me way again.

all
good things
begin

outdoors

Notes from a Garden

Mary Hackett

"And here," I said, "is where I imagine the pergola." 'Here' was the south-west corner of my fifteen-metre square of roll-out lawn. I was surprised but pleased at Karynn Jarrett-McCormac's reaction. She gasped. A squeaky kind of gasp.

"Full size?" she asked.

The question threw me, I admit. What size do pergolas come in? Can they be ordered in large, medium and small? With Ms Jarrett-McCormac's gold Parker pen poised over her Muji clipboard, hesitation would be fatal.

"Full size of course." I said. The Royal Horticultural Society's Directory of Garden Design recommended a pergola for the introduction of strong horizontal lines and design structure. Ms Jarrett-McCormac and I were as one in our view that this garden needed line and structure.

"Of course." said Karynn Jarrett-McCormac. She wrote it down.

"I do think chinoiserie is so now," she said.

Karynn Jarrett-McCormac knows about things Chinese. Her photomontage 'The Yangtze Delta: Thoughts on the direction of horticulture for a new millennium,' was the highlight of the Saile Valley Horticultural Society's Spring programme. I went twice. It was inspiring.

We agreed that chinoiserie is exactly now. Ms. Jarrett-McCormac is designing a circular garden for Hampton Court next summer. Structures will all face towards the magnetic north in homage to the compass. The Chinese, it appears, invented the compass. I must have missed that reference in 'Thoughts on the direction of horticulture for a new millennium'.

"Chinoiserie," murmured Karynn Jarrett-McCormac again, hissing the "sh" through her slightly protuberant front teeth. "Such a charming conceit."

She drew a diagram on her clipboard. Without my glasses it was a bit of a blur.

"It has been too long since I did a pagoda" sighed Karynn Jarrett-McCormac. She almost purred.

The pergola was everywhere in Chelsea last year. I noticed one in the Renaissance garden and in Diarmuid's patch and I am quite sure someone said it was featured in the Jardin Sauvage. I suppose it does take a certain vision to extrapolate from the Chelsea concept to suburban reality. Look through your heart to find beauty, that's my motto. My heart saw pergola.

We moved towards the north wall. I fancied a green border here. Shades of green, from lime to kale, harmonising against yellow Seskin brick. We would have cordyline and treeferns, solomon's seal and bergenia.

"Oh no," said Karynn Jarrett-McCormac, "This will be the bamboo thicket."

My diagram for a green bed, cypress to the back, alchemilla mollis frothing to the front, crumbled around me. But I am a lateral thinker. That workshop on Garden Illumination in Frascati last summer may have been a little expensive but it gave me context within which I could contribute to the Jarrett-McCormac scenario.

"With up-lighting." I proffered. Strategically placed, low voltage light fixtures to give the bamboos a soft glow, adding to their enchantment. Should we include a sound system? I got quite enthusiastic about it all.

But up-lighting was not Karynn Jarrett-McCormac. "Bamboos swaying in the slightest zephyr," she half-whispered. "Shadows dancing on a summer evening. Wind chimes. Recessed bullet lights in the wall with Japanese lanterns for special occasions." My garden supremo was hitting her stride. "And dragons. With the pagoda as focal point we need dragons".

I had no idea that dragons were essential to pergolas but these are the details a top-notch garden designer can contribute to a design.

I abandoned up-lighting. "Dragons" I agreed. "Plenty of dragons. In several sizes."

"I have a wonderful man," said Karynn Jarrett-McCormac wiping her pebble glasses. "A truly, wonderful little man who specialises in genuine Burmese garden antiquities. I am going to introduce you two. I feel you share the same soul."

I was awed. Karynn Jarrett-McCormac's contacts are legendary. I may bring selected Garden Circle colleagues to meet the Burmese importer. Perhaps on my second visit. When the rapport between his soul and mine will be evident.

"The last time I was in he had the most extraordinary pair of dragon finales, inlaid with lapis lazuli, garnet eyes, amazing craftsmanship." Karynn Jarrett-McCormac was sweeping on. "I can see them, spotlit, benign guardians of your portal." Inspiration was flowing, the clipboard balanced precariously on my soon-to-be-removed sundial, the gold pen racing across the page.

I could see them too. I have felt their presence several times since.

"We must have water." said Karynn Jarrett-McCormac.

Water was exactly what we needed. I was about to say so myself.

"A rill," I offered. Garden Design for the New Century – presented over three weekends at Harrow Hall last winter – recommended rills. I could visualise the garden in July. Sunlight filtering through vine leaves, striking sparks from the water below. The rush and bubble of my stream, cool in the noonday heat.

I might add jasmine to the vitis coignetiae winding through the pillars. Or, perhaps, honeysuckle.

"Not a rill." said Karynn Jarrett-McCormac with a shudder. "Rills are certainly not of now. We need something Zen, something to encourage clarity of mind. We are defined by the Buddhist influence of that pagoda. Rills are shallow. We are tapping into the deep wisdom that comes from going beyond the concerns of self."

I was silenced. A rivulet running under dappled shade was, I could see, a rather commonplace concept. With Karynn Jarrett-McCormac one aspired to higher things.

"An ink pool." Karynn Jarrett-McCormac said.

"Ink?"

"Black as night, mysterious as the Orient. Gaze within and the outer world fades away."

"This will be under the pergola?" I asked. I had some difficulty visualising it. Could an ink pool reflect vine leaves? Would an ink pool have goldfish?

"Directly," said Ms Jarrett-McCormac briskly.

"Reflecting the creepers?" I hazarded.

"If you wish," said Karynn Jarrett-McCormac graciously. "A rather baroque touch that, strangler vines embracing the perpendicular, but I love the macabre, don't you?"

"Black water?" I said. I wanted to understand this clearly.

"Inky black. A lacquered black basin filled with distilled water to which scented essence of china ink is added twice a week. I have done this with selected clients already," said Karynn Jarrett-McCormac closing her eyes the better to recall, "and I can assure you they are ecstatic. Mrs B in particular. Her garden has been included in County Gardens of Merit on the basis of my ink pool alone. Without a pagoda."

Mrs B's inclusion in County Gardens of Merit is well known. She mentions it at most Garden Show committee meetings.

I had to sit down. Karynn Jarrett-McCormac's inspired concept overwhelmed me. She had tapped into cosmic harmony, framed twenty-first century irony in spiritual perspective. I could imagine international interest. A spread in Interiors magazine. Perhaps a television crew or two. A visit from the Garden Landscapers' Association of which Mrs B is an honorary member.

We sat side by side on the garden bench which will be replaced, as soon as I have a moment to visit that importer, by something antique from Burma. Karynn Jarrett-McCormac's busy fingers tapped out costings on her laptop. It was a pleasure to sign the specification sheet.

Karynn Jarrett-McCormac promised to be on site next week to begin excavations. I can hardly wait.

A Grave at the End of the World

Deborah Ballard

I wanted a grave at the end of the world
Where there's no further to go
And no more to discover.
My friends would pile up stones,
A cairn to wear time,
Sing me to rest with hero songs,
And swear perdition to my enemies.

I wanted a pyre like a beacon
Shouting my name for miles around,
From my fat and bones,
My hair flying up in sparks,
One last yell into the darkness
Before I am gone forever.

And libations of good wine,
And sacrifices – not hecatombs,
But a fatted calf would be good,
A fine feast for my friends;
A party under the stars, in short
As I go up in smoke.

I would leave more quietly now,
Bury me in a shallow grave
Under the pear tree in the orchard,
Minding not to harm its roots.
My love will sit with me a while
Under Spring's foam of blossom,
And eat pears sweetened by my decay.

Set no headstone on my grave:
I will live for a while in the memory
Of those who knew me.
Plant snowdrops over my body
So that those who come after
Will know not to dig there, till
My bones have crumbled into mould.

The snowdrops may outlast me
Returning each year with the pale sun,
Or the plough may dismember me
Or the land return to bog.
When even my name is forgotten,
I shall die at last; until that time,
I would not lie heavy on the earth.

Double Blades

Eileen Kavanagh

In the photograph we could be anywhere there's snow and ice and winter's naked trees. This particular photograph is an odd shape and its hue is strangely brilliant. Maybe Nana lent us her Polaroid, yet why would we take a camera ice-skating? It's just one of those family mysteries that will remain frozen in time. I guess I am about seven, as I come up to Mom's shoulder and Dad's waist. Mom is definitely a couple of winter seasons out of fashion in her white mohair hat and striped woollen trousers. Dad and I are a clash of pinks and reds. The ice is snowcovered and full of the patterns of skaters. No Zamboni to clear away all the impressions on this lake. My blades leave a strange imprint as my parents insisted on renting me the double-bladed skates. Although they are fearful for my safety, a few weeks further into the winter my older brother will break through this ice. In his eagerness to make a save he will skate too near the Danger Thin Ice sign and weighted down by his goalie paraphernalia he will be quickly pulled under.

What if I had never skated with the double-blades? If I'd had the kind of parents who believed falling down was much less of a problem than picking yourself up. Now, almost four decades later, I guess that I'd be able to do a couple of jumps or at least cross one skate over the other.

Rationing Compassion

Conor Ferguson

Last week I was waiting for the bus. Next to me was this gorgeous girl. I turned to see her face properly and saw that she was crying. I didn't know what to do. Next thing I found myself putting an arm around her. No-one said anything. She put her face against my neck. I could feel her warm tears welling in my collar bone. When her bus came I told her everything would be all right. Then yesterday, at the same bus stop, I saw someone else crying. It was an old guy. I just left him to it.

Falling into Place

John Edmondson

The sun, well down behind the trees,
still warms the great walled garden
with its centuries of secrets
inviting me to stay and share.

As bats whirr jagged overhead,
by choosing my spot carefully,
I change the way the branches look.
Their greeny black trapeziums
turn into stronger triangles
and lock my jigsaw down,
the missing central piece
a strangely rounded shape.

Soft cigars of cloud fly slow,
pearl above, bright pink below,
and, confident of what will follow,
wave off the hapless weathermen.

A star, once seen, flames brighter.
High ice broken, the rest peep out –
here and there, then all at once.
The jet trail drips to nothing.

The wall, wise, high, cuts out all trace
of fripperies, conceits, pretentious pace
and lies of life outside. It's dark.
A late dog settles down somewhere.

Sure of my rightful place
in mind, in time, in space,
a good position
perfectly triangulated by owls.

Glory Boy 2006

Eoin Cavanagh

Listening to canteen talk, I dug out
My Astro-Turf boots from the hall cupboard
I'd been at Aikido the whole year
Fit and poised, conscious of my centre
I surprised myself with a one-eighty pivot
Side-step and low curving shot.

Maybe I should have come out of retirement earlier
Rather than wait for Maldini to quit,
Zidane's last hurrah. I bet in school
Zizou was always given the ball
A pillar of hope for the lanky bastards.

At twelve I made left-full my own.
I was prone to nosebleeds and didn't like the cold.
One rainy day, one-nil down against Oldcourt
I pushed up into the box, and the left mid-fielder
Too timid to shoot, or spotting my run
Played me in, I slid the ball one-touched
Past the hapless incumbent of the green
Into the right-hand corner of the net
Muller's goal in '72 meant less.

This was the days before video, and everyone forgot
Except me and our midfield dynamo, who we admired
Because his father played League of Ireland, 'in the day,'
Who pointed out that my subsequent back-heel led
To Oldcourt's winner.

Notwithstanding that, I strode into the sitting room, hair
                                    mud-stained,
proud as a peach.
My Dad, my brother and the neighbours
Circled the colour screen, immersed in rugby that finished

Ireland- 7, France-7
Early in the Five Nations, we won every other game
Close to a grand slam, but not, not ever...

On the Astro Turf
I continue to impress
If only myself
With drag-backs and turns, a diagonal slide-rule ball
A last ditch block. Entertaining as it is,
It's jokey, sunny, antiseptic.
Olympic divers marked for style.
Like a lump in my throat, I miss the mud, the wet, the bite.
The Glory passes, never to return,
As William Shatner knew, and now Zidane.

The Triathalon

Maresa Sheehan

In the river with all its swirling brown silt
Must be like how a raisin feels
In a cake with the wooden spoon mixing,
Globbing the goo around and on top of its back
Galumpsh galumpsh

W-whuu-uuhah a heaving of its wrinkled skin out
And onto the bike: a far cry now from the taut
Grape in its moulded melted-on bubbly bit
Of a bubble-wrap skin as it's landed into the cake tin
After a cooling dizzy spin on the spoon
Feeling like when it was in a truck once going
Over a bump in the road and being in the air
For a second and that sucky-in feeling
In the pit of its pulp.

In the oven now, oh God the heat
but at least the swirling has stopped
and the ground is firming underneath.

October

Samantha McCaffrey

A shock of yellow,
strobes of it,
interrupt green.
Leaf corpses lie,
the first fallen in battle,
among the bloodstained rotten berries.
Something from above
is bombing the ground with chestnuts.
Everywhere is a warzone.
The trees, dressed in mould and gold,
cake and crackle,
but don't talk about the victims.

When you strip down naked,
your orange insides fall out.
And your pips,
spot and pop the carpeted earth.
I stamp out the embers
on all this burning rubbish,
but I can find no pacing pulse.
This morning
everything is falling apart.

The Garden

Conor Ferguson

At the end of the garden autumn leaves are burning
Russet and gold, ochres of yellow and red;
Sluttish scarlet like the shoes I once spied,
Peeping out from under the bed.

At the end of the garden a shroud of smoke looms,
Like a memory not remembered well.
Of you with your silly broom,
Swooshing and brushing the leaves
In the gloom.

(A futile attempt to take control of things?
Or wilfully wasting time, as I waited,
Impatient, forgotten, in the wings.)

At the end of the garden a fire burns.
Orange leaves urged by destiny to dust.
And a hedgehog waddles out
Reluctantly bound for nowhere, slowly,
A warning in its heart that things don't last.

But now the air is clear, the garden bare
The leaves gone, your broom forlorn.
A charcoal scar marks where you once loved,
And it slowly dawns that this is the end
Of the garden.

Second Hand Evening – Parnell Square

Helena Nolan

This Autumn sky has been washed and mended many times
The clouds pinned across it
Like developing photographs
Their faces shifting
In the Northern wind

This lozenge of light dissolves slowly in water
The lamplight of ages
Like a twirling kaleidoscope
Its glass doors folding
With infinite grace

This square and church
The streets dead and buried
Stake out an ancient perimeter
Under shoe-smooth stones
Over fossilised strata
Of calcified lives

This Autumn sky has been washed and mended many times
Pegged out to dry on cables
It bellies in the wind
Clouds for its pockets
For buttons, the stars.

The Fire Escape

Yvonne Cullen

Such rain
on the metal landings
under security lights
rain's funnelled pour.
Siren that means
some business
and all this sodium-glow.
Crowds enter night-class below here
on a night after hard times
how still it is regardless
of the rain.
Roofs
found where they were by it
shine, and the odd window
lit as you are
lit after hard times.

Ice
James Stafford

When he could lie quietly no longer, the boy got up. He slipped out of bed in the grey half-light, and put on yesterday's clothes that lay in a pile on the cold linoleum. Walking softly on the landing, he saw the light under the door of his father's room.

The man slept in his clothes, a shoe-box of old photographs beside him on the bed. There were other things in there as well, the boy knew: theatre programmes; a newspaper cutting with a picture of a young couple; old hand-written airline ticket stubs, the letters in red waxy pencil almost rubbed away. He lay on his side, a silk scarf knotted up in the hand against his chin. The boy covered him with a quilt, and kissed his cheek, which was rough with three days' growth: red, shot through with grey. His father's breath smelled faintly of whiskey, and there was the perfume of the scarf: not just the scent of perfume or powder, but something more familiar, and very soft.

The house was dark; and quiet, apart from the ticking of the hall clock, and the big old fridge, humming away in the kitchen. As he made his way silently downstairs, the boy breathed in softly through his nose; by the time he reached the back door, he could feel his heart thumping in his ears, and his chest felt like he was deep under water.

The bolt of the door shot back with a clunk, and he exhaled deeply. His breath hung in the air in front of him as he stood on the threshold. Everything had changed, yet it looked just the same. Fat flakes of snow were settling here and there, and the garden was quiet under a soft white blanket. His father's work shirts from the week before were steeping in a bucket of ice by the door. There was a plaid cuff visible through the ice, frozen into a salute. He lifted the bucket inside the door to thaw, and set off.

He hunched his shoulders against the icy breeze. He had borrowed his father's razor the day before, and his face felt strange: bare and too smooth. The flagstones of the yard were difficult to walk upon; the loose chippings of the road would be easier. He looked down the hill at the bottom of the garden: the tarmac road would take him into the village, where there were people he knew, shops, his school, the church in its grounds where the clay looked undisturbed under the flowers. He did not want to go that way yet. He turned away and followed the lane up and across the fields towards the lake.

The cold air hurt his lungs, and his feet crunched on the gravel as he climbed the hill. The way was steep, and he wished he had worn boots, instead of his new black shoes. He kept his eyes on the ground so he could see where he was going, and he would not become dizzy looking up at the summit. When he reached the top, he stood and looked around him.

The condensation trail of an airliner cut across the pale sky. He could just make out the silvery wings flying high and fast, the needle-sharp jets of water vapour trailing behind until they merged into a cloud and faded away. The air was solid enough to take the weight of a plane, and sharp enough to sting like a knife, but someone could disappear and it would collapse softly into the space they left behind.

He looked back at the quiet house. For days it had been full of strangers who all knew his name, and looked at him full of pity, as though he were on top of a burning building and they were unable to reach him. The rooms were hot and noisy; his face blazed, and his throat ached; he overheard people talking about him. The voices were deafening, like a radio tuned to no particular station but turned up so loud that the speaker grille vibrated with static.

When they all went away, the big red-haired man sobbed quietly, in his room, while the boy lay awake on the other side of the wall, the blankets over his head.

The lake beneath him formed in a hollow where the river was trapped between the hills on its way to the sea. His father had a small boat there, and sometimes they went fishing together. His father had a length of hosepipe filled with lead shot, which he used to stun the fish once they were landed, so that they would die quickly, and not drown in the air.

One summer, he learned to swim in the lake, where the water was clear and still. The first time he was taken to the beach he cried. The water was not the same as the lake: it stung his eyes, and swept him off his feet; and when he swallowed it, it was salty and it made him sick. They brought sandwiches, wrapped in bread paper. He only drank milk at home, but at the beach he preferred tea: the plastic cup of the flask was almost too hot to hold, and he liked the way cool drops collected in the screw thread at the rim.

It began to snow more heavily. The boy wished that he could stay forever on top of the hill, looking at the water and the sky, and that the snow would fall gently from the sky and cover him like a blanket. He ran his sleeve across his face; his eyes were red, and they stung from the cold and the tears. He began to retrace his steps down the hill towards home.

Something made him look back towards the lake. Out of the corner of his eye, he saw something flash on its smooth dark surface, and he remembered a question he had once asked. Could a mermaid leave the salt water of the sea and swim upriver? Would she hold her breath, or drown in the cold, dry air?

Just Running

Maresa Sheehan

Running with only her heart and her legs
weaving through elephant-footed trunks
with cones and needles in their toes.
She's more foot than bar stool, vibrating
like an incoming text message.

Frightening a calf as she whizzes by
his yellow tags shaking from his upside
flight out of his dry crunchy site.
Her thighs more chicken nugget than pork
Loins gliding like a well-worn step machine.

Swooshing through the hairbrush forest
head down not thinking of Fionn Mac Cumhail
– flicking not cracking a twig or a branch –
Her mind more instant than percolated
a small terrier dog out running in the rain.

all
good things
begin

elsewhere

The Woman on the Square

James Stafford

I brace myself in a corner of the basket and lean out. My left arm behind me, is hooked around the mooring rope; my right reaches out as far as it will go. I am trying to catch something. My hand moves through the air like a wing, dispersing the clouds without ever touching them. They pass beneath my palm, and in the brief turbulence they scatter their little grey shadows far below.

In late spring, people have become accustomed to spending time outside on the square, and they look up as I pass over. There is a terrace filled with tables, and a boy runs in a slow arc across the cobbles, the shadows of his outstretched arms like a bird in the late evening sun. I shut out the creaking of the wicker and the rigging, and I can hear the noises and laughter from below. Over the whistling wind, and my own breath, I hear a name. I look over my shoulder. There is no-one there.

Someone is waving from the café. She calls, "Fly, Charlie, fly!"

My glass is overflowing; they always do this here, and I don't know why. The beer is strong and sticky, and the waiter is ignoring people fluently in many languages. There is a woman by herself at a table. "Here you are," she says, and she gives me her paper napkin. The bar is busy, but the other people are out of focus, lost in the noise on the terrace. She has a glass of something red, like vermouth. She looks like she should have a cat. "Puss, puss," she whispers, handing something down from the table. I prefer dogs, myself. "Good fellow, sit," she says, "My little Cavalier." I offer her a cigarette, fumbling with the paper matchbook. "Should you really be smoking at your age?" she asks.

"Must you go?" I hear someone say from the bar. "Please stay," she says, but it is late, and the city is already grey and misty, like an old photo.

I am walking close to the wall with my head in a book. People bump into me, as gently as brushing cobwebs, but I need to be able to find my way, to work out how many paces there are to the width of a finger. If I lose my place, I could end up miles away.

She is sitting at a table on the terrace. She has a drink in front of her.

"Where did you go?" she asks me.

"I'm sorry. I had things to do."

"Was there an important telegram?"

"No."

"Your parachute was beautiful. Charlotte and I waved at you as you came down to land."

Now and again, I stop to look at some of the things that people have dropped. They are like bookmarks: tickets, receipts, and scraps torn from postcards. All of the important things have turned into the soft grey dust that lies in the folds and creases. Echoes of thoughts cover the walls like faded graffiti done in chalk.

"Where can I go now?" she asks. "You have been abroad. Before you came here, I saw you looking down from your balloon."

I tell her that there is nowhere quite like this.

"The wedding party has just left, and I don't think that I can stay here any longer. There is no-one left now."

"But I need you here," I say. "Otherwise, who will I talk to?"

The terrace is quiet. There are people in the doorway, silently waiting.

"You've changed," she says, and she stops and thinks. "No, maybe it wasn't you, but someone who looked like you. You have a good accent. Were you here during the war?" I tell her I have been coming here for almost twenty years, now. "I think I would like to go for a walk. Will you take me?" The way out of the Grand Place is narrow, and lined with small shops. We pass the cathedral and come out onto the boulevard. It runs straight and wide, bordered by trees, until it reaches the end of the map where there is no more paper. I sit with my finger marking a spot on the page as I lean against a stack of old books and dangle one leg through the trapdoor of the attic.

The Foundling

(Tree root carving in Wat Mahathat, Ayuthaya)

Helena Nolan

They found your face
In a tree root
'Unearthed' is the perfect word for it
What a gasp of discovery
You must have caused
Your head embedded
In the knotted wood
Your plaited hair like vines
Your eyes as blank as eggs
While fingers plucked at you
Revealing more and more
Of your design
From the greedy mud.
Now that you have been
Cleansed and polished to perfection
Primed for public display
Their only concern
Is how to move you
To a more suitable location
Without having to move the tree
And if they do remove it
Will those aged roots
That nourished you
Curl up in fright
And send their terrified hormones
To your naked head
So that great cracks might ravage you
And pulverise your sheltered skin
Still innocent as stone
But prone perhaps
To terrible decay
Once your foster host begins to quiver?
Their dilemma then

Is how best to showcase
Your undeniable gifts
Here on the forest floor
Where perhaps a cluster
Of citizens might come
Once in a lifetime
With a suitable guide
If money enough could be found
Or the ultimate risk
To sever you
To lift you up
To a place so much better
The very sight of it
May ravish you
With the yearning
For your ancient, wooded world.

A Great Noise

Stephen Bailey

Eventually the sun rose on the small town. The few skinny chickens that still lingered pecked hopefully at the sun-baked earth. The old dog lifted a painful eyelid. He had dragged himself into the courtyard an hour before sunset, leaving a trail of blood in his wake. The sun had stirred the sky a matching crimson as it sank away, glad to be drawing to a close that most awful of days. The dog was called Rubber because when he had been a pup the children had been able to bend his legs into such funny positions. Now one of his legs was missing and his fur was ragged and singed. The blast wave had thrown him thirty feet. The chickens and the remaining pig stood still and watched as the old dog bled without a sound and his eyes became grey and still. Above, silhouetted against the sun, the vultures circled lower.

The emu walked slowly, awkwardly around the farmyard blinking with her one remaining eye. Here and there she stopped and held her high head almost proudly. No other farms in the surrounding countryside had an emu. She had been happy mulling this fact over in her uncomplicated mind for the last few years of her contented life. Preening in the kitchen window and enjoying the attentions of the village children took up much of her time. Now it was different. The children were gone and a strange silence hung over the farm. The great noise had left her unable to see on one side of everything and she wandered circling and confused, catching sight of half-seen phantoms. As she often did, she had been sunning herself at the back of the greenhouse when the commotion began. She hadn't heard a word of sense from anyone since.

"They're calling it an apostrophe," she said to a friend on the phone a few days later, "the work of fundie mentholists." Nobody knew she could use the phone.

Apart from the injured animals and the ones too shell-shocked to speak or eat or to move at all, there were 'the talkers' who wanted 'to make sense of it all.' In this particular farmyard it was – perhaps surprisingly – the mice who were most vocal. The mice had been either lost in the middle of grain sacks, between planks of wood, or taking turns gnawing the cork from the wine cask in the cellar. Their ranks had suffered the least damage from the shrapnel wave.

The mice with their small knowledge of the world sat unafraid in the sunshine. They talked at length about the moment of 'The Great Noise', the time before it and the time after. They spoke in detail about right and wrong and about how things had been in the past and why things were like they were now, and how they would be in the future. And nobody spoke of the cows.

Others were not so fortunate. The great prize Clydesdale had always liked to watch the cows' noisy trundle through the village to the dairy. He stood each day at the stone wall to await their procession towards the town. A nine-inch piece of metal from the milk trolley had passed straight through his neck all but beheading him. When they could eventually talk, some of the ducks said they had seen Big Victor's head sliced off even before they heard the great booming noise or felt the great wind. His blood formed a pool in the middle of the yard that went from bright red to black over a few days. The flies came and hovered and dipped frantically over it. But no one ever spoke to the flies.

The ducks – gifted with wings and quick reactions – had spent the slow moments of noisy inferno flapping in mid-air. Flapping pot-luck for hot stinging metal. Only one of their rank had been caught. Eric was a runaway who had flown from a nearby village a year before declaiming his eternal love for one of the pretty white ducks. Eric, a romantic, lost a wing and a foot and died declaring his love for the same duck. Marie, the object of his affections, hated him and always ignored him but was said to retell sobbingly the tale of his death for many a year after it. For all the animals this is a tale of woe.

The people had always said the carpenter was a walking pun because he had a chip on his shoulder. Afterwards they were no kinder saying he was a limping pun. The carpenter lost a leg in what the townsfolk came to know as 'The Attack'. He had spent the day mumbling to himself and paring down a piece of wood for an ornate gazebo. He grew warm as he worked and his sweat stained dark patches on his work shirt.

He looked forward to a cool glass of beer when he could agree with himself that he had done enough with the day. From where he worked at his bench he had a good view of the street and the church and the dairy. From time to time he would stop and blow the sawdust from his arm and watch with his pensive demeanour the day's goings on. The carpenter noticed The Strangers at what he reckoned to be about midday and, distracted, he nicked his thumb straining to look at them.

By all accounts, The Strangers looked out of place in the village. Strangers were rare and the odd hobo type who wandered through was easily identified as such. The Strangers that day were different. Those who noticed them said they seemed to have a slow and easy way about them, not fitting for people in an unfamiliar place. Their eyes were placid; calm like the eyes of old men who sit on porches at dusk to smoke and talk about their youth.

The Strangers stood by the church for a while, then strolled – lazily it seemed – along by the dairy stopping briefly beside one of the fences designed to corral the cows inside. The man stooped to fill a water vessel at the trough and the carpenter thought it strange and almost offered them fresh water. The carpenter swore later that the stranger left the vessel by the trough and walked away, up the street and out of sight.

"Something just didn't feel right 'bout that," he said, "Poor man don't forget his water on a hot day. I figured them for drunks."

Almost directly across the road, the town's librarian looked out on another day without incident. She finished stamping the new arrivals with the county seal and turned her attention to the carpenter's premises. She had always had what she understood was called 'a crush' on the woodworker, but nobody else knew, except for perhaps the old crow, to whom she had once drunkenly admitted it. The librarian would later detail to friends how The Strangers visited the library and looked through the shelves of books quietly.

She could not give descriptions of them to those who asked but said they were, 'so ordinary, so peaceful I suppose…' as to not merit any attempt at interrogatory conversation. They left as quietly as they had come and the librarian admitted she was, "glad to have the place to myself again," as she explained they were 'kinda creepy.' Later, after the attack, she helped nurse the carpenter back to full strength and secretly hoped he would repay her by courting her and perhaps even a proposal. But the carpenter returned to his quiet vigil by his workbench. He was slower now and looked out on the street with the sad angry eyes of those that have suffered injustice.

The lodger was perhaps more helpful. The lodger was a wanderer who had been in the village for a month or more at the time and had travelled extensively around the parts. He claimed to have seen The Strangers before and claimed a foreknowledge of disaster when he saw them arrive in the village (it is not documented however, that he told anyone). The lodger claimed to have seen the couple before in a village two days away. He remembered thinking it strange to see a young couple without children and travelling so light. That night he asked after them at the bar and was told it was thought that they were miners heading north as they had bought a quantity of dynamite.

"Hard times these are," he said to the proprietor over a glass of whiskey, "When a man is without children and must bring his wife to the mine."

After the attack the lodger took no more pleasure from his ramblings. He stayed around the numbed town not talking to anyone and drinking whiskey but not eating. He died some months later. For the humans also, this is a tale of woe.

"Well, if I were the type to dwell on things," the barman was known to say when asked about that day, "I guess I wouldn't have many customers. All I remember is it was a normal, hot, quiet afternoon one minute and then boom! There's a sound like thunder in a valley and the windows are all red and there's a weird ruddy light streaming in. I thought it were an earthquake 'til I felt the stillness after it. Deadly quiet and red ooze streaming down the windows. For a moment, in that eerie light and silence, I thought all our times had finally come."

Opening the door of his premises the barman saw the severed head of a heifer lying on its side, blinking and tongue-tied. He saw two dozen or more cattle in various states of dismemberment, dead or dying. In between these lay the bloody and mutilated corpses of humans. Of people he knew personally. He recognised his sister by the floral print of her dress, but half of her was gone. To this day his establishment is called The Cows' Blood Inn due to its proximity to the catastrophe. For a while many of the townspeople objected to this title but by then the name had already stuck.

The person who can best recount a story is usually the one with the highest vantage point of events and in this tale – as in many – it is a bird. The Old Crow had been cranky all day as he usually was during hot weather. He had tried hiding from the sun under the ledge of the church belfry, under the trees by the lake and even in the old ruin, all to no avail.

"The day of The Great Noise," he would say in later years, 'was a day to make the black run from your wings.'

If invited (as he invariably was) to continue, he would stretch his wings and settle himself before looking somewhere into the distance and continuing thus:

"I remember it was hot. I was riding the thermals above the village trying to cool down when I saw them. My vision was as good then as it remains today and I remember seeing far off on the southerly road, two strangers appear. How did I know they were strangers I hear you ask? Well that's how well I could see on that clear haze free day. They weren't folk I'd seen round the village and I've been here since before most of you."

So the crow would go on when asked. From his point of view (and there is not much point in disputing it as the ducks could not have flown as high and there were no other birds in the village that day) the events took place quickly and deliberately. Two strangers apparently arrived alone and after spending some time around the main street and saying nothing to anyone, they headed out of town. For many years afterwards animals from near and far came to the farmyard to hear the Old Crow recount his tale. He became something of a minor celebrity and although many claimed the story changed from one telling to the next, he was always entertaining.

"About a mile or so out of town," he would continue to his captive audience, "The Strangers stopped and sat down at the big oak at the fork in the road. Now I wouldn't've given them much more interest than you give to most humans had I not noticed them kneel together and begin to pray silently. Now prayer – that most human of indulgences – is usually confined to the church, but as you all know, humans are a strange animal, so I was content to let this pass as plain old quirkiness."

"Besides," he would add, "by now I could see the Widow Jenkins was making so as to feed her roosters and I was all of a mind to swoop down sudden like and raid their feast. Just then I noticed The Strangers had risen again and were holding each other in a long embrace."

"These folk been in the sun too long," I was thinking. Next they proceeds to undress slowly and careful like and help each other into some new form of clothing. They carefully lined packs of small brown parcels around their bodies and when they were done they put their clothes back on, embraced again and started walking together two metres apart towards the centre of the village.'

A hush would now descend on the gathered animals as they remembered what happened next on that fateful day. Those who had survived bowed their heads, remembering fallen friends. Victor the great Clydesdale and Eric the duck and even Rubber the dog.

"When The Strangers reached the centre of town," The Old Crow would continue slowly, his voice heavy and croaking with the memory, "they threw off their mortal masks and showed their true form of fire and blood and anger. They took the cows and many of the humans with them in a great ball of fury. They left us animals injured, blinded and dumbstruck. They left the human children in the street screaming, bloody and searching for their dead parents. Man and animal suffered equally on that day. Yes, for all the living it was surely a day of woe."

Each evening the sun sets on the small town. In appearance it is much the same, except for the gaping space where the dairy once stood. The animals go about their daily lives and remember and wonder. It is the people who show the difference more acutely. They are more suspicious and less carefree. Strangers are not welcome. In the cooling of the evening, when the old men sit on the porches they are often silent. They know their own lives are almost at an end but they worry for their children and their grandchildren and each night the glow of the sunset reminds them of the ruddy hue of spilt blood.

Guest-Book

Yvonne Cullen

(i)

Notes from the Demesne

Sometimes it was one stand of pines we watched there.
The horizon bald but for them.

We were the figures who struggled on old bikes
or pulled a child along the track, then.

Sometimes we drove the car that passed.
Then others – as much for us – went on through their own stories there.

Or storms had thrown heights down. In those woods
everything pointed after them.

Then
It was a bowed birch we were looking for again.
The trunk burst out

to damage's only almost-stilled
wood knives, its wooden feathers.

What colour that wood had healed to we
were going to see,
for some good that did us.

(ii)

Reception Centre

Days came
and we woke – guests that we were –
rooms we wouldn't long have: steadily screened in us,

or it was us filming against loss: so much
brick dust in the shutter-casing.

Believed

we would always be here.
(Then we were folding back shutters, seeing the near trees,
and the sky was yellow).

Sometimes we left the house, and the April day shocked us with
– it could have been anything –

but say it was cold,
and to be surprised was to be already dead
watching only others' breath drift

as they queued at a phone-box outside
with the patience of horses.

(iii)
Wake Up

Or (still no nearer to our lives than to a cup we carried here)
didn't we each walk back
more than once

to rooms with walls lit green while we'd been gone
(by leaf-light and moss-light from the trees coming in
                                        without need of us)

and were home before the door-saddle of a room.
And didn't such comfort come, as warmly, when

at windows, on the road
our eyes combed the view for what could mean us:

found, below trees. the dark
keeps us coats that are ours,
not for us yet, as

when in the day room

- the arm of the stereo let out -

before a Bach choir sings "Wachet Auf"
a flaw throws a before-echo of first notes

and we're home in the wish to start out now
even if it is too soon.

(iv)
Reports

Some days we left the house and
                        sun showed the
creased arms of our coats on paths, said the
closest to life we get is a dreaming edge
                        where we meet our shadows with our skin,
is the edge of the world that will not need us.

Mirror Image
Frances Plunkett Russell

I was always at home and welcome in "Au Père Tranquil"; a regular, alone sometimes but amongst friends. I raised my glass to old George as he settled himself on the stool at the other end of the bar. He mopped his forehead and said,

"Paris is on fire today. Too much for my poor Mitzy."

He patted his dog's head and asked Henri, the bartender for a Ricard with ice and a bowl of water for the dog. He lifted his newspaper. Henri topped up my glass and inquired,

"Claude away?"

"Yes! He is in La Rochelle, but back tomorrow."

"Ah! Bon! Bon! La Rochelle is a very nice place."

"Yes! It is. I went with him last month but this time I had too much work on, so...."

I had told Claude that La Rochelle reminded me of Howth in Ireland.

"Except that Howth is much more spectacular," I said.

"You must bring me back with you and I will see if you are right or not. Will you bring me back to meet your family too maybe?"

My heart skipped and jumped like that of a girl. That glorious week, he had hinted at marriage and I mentioned babies. We had been so busy since then somehow.

I lifted my eyes to the mirror and blinked as I caught sight of a woman standing, waiting to cross the street. She wore a rich combination of cinnamon and chocolate colours which looked cool and fresh in the afternoon heat. She stepped into the street, as I turned from the mirror to look at her directly through the open window. Was it really Marcella Edwards from Dublin? It couldn't be I thought. She lived in the United States now. I swung around as she approached the bar, and watched her in the mirror again. She eased her slim behind into a wicker seat outside under the awning and turned her back to me.

I tried to count the years since I had last seen her, but her presence was distracting me.

"You okay?" Henri asked.

"Yes! I just saw a ghost, I think."

I tapped my glass and he filled it, looking at me with anxious eyes.

I smiled and he walked away.

Marcella still had that shock of thick red hair but the coils and loops of childhood were absent. That hair was smoother and tamer now. As she turned to catch the waiter's eye, I noticed that her complexion too seemed paler; it had a translucent quality which gave her a look of fragility that was undeserved.

Those grey eyes, so often lifted to me in triumph, were shielded that evening, like mine, in sunglasses. The faint trace of her voice brought tumbling remembrances of our childhood and adolescence, none of them positive. She smoked a cigarette through a long slim holder. I thought that her imperious expression concealed an unease at being alone. Marcella had always surrounded herself with sycophants. What was she doing here? I hoped she was just a tourist. For a moment then, I considered launching myself at her, catching her off guard, throwing her into turmoil. I would demand an apology; get her to admit that she was a liar after all. I smiled to myself, my eyes on her, mesmerised.

When Marcella came to live in Howth as a child, she told us that she hated her name. At her command we called her Marcie. She was American, exotic, rich and different. The only Americans we knew were on the television. Then we discovered that her father, who had had a shock of white hair, actually came to Ireland to work in the fledgling national television station. He knew all the stars. Her mother had a dreamy vagueness about her and was a writer, we were told. They had a maid and a nanny who lived in a small flat at the side of the house. The house itself had underfloor central heating, in contrast to our coal fires; a playroom filled with unusual toys including two rocking horses for the twins; a games room with a billiard table and bar that had a white carpet. To enter we had to take off our shoes.

They moved in on my twelfth birthday and my mother invited the entire family to my party. When Mother discovered that Marcella and I shared the day, she suggested that we blow out the candles together. I became Marcella's special friend then. I remained important to her for a while too, until she found someone more worthy of her increasing stature in the village. All through my teenage years I hung on the edge of what became her crowd, never being accepted but always hoping. It was Marcella too, who began the taunting of me about my name, causing me to hate it for years.

"Scarlett," Marcella would say, exaggerating her southern drawl, "Oh my! Scarlett! Did Mama think you think you would grow up with movie star good looks? Did she really think giving you that name meant you would turn out to look like Vivian Leigh then? Oh my, my, Miss Scarlett."

Then the others, coached by her, would chorus.

"Well now, Miss Scarlett! Frankly we don't give a damn."

There they would leave me on the cusp, jarred and bitter. My mother, a simple kind woman, loved the movies and my hurt was as much for her as for myself.

Ironically it was Marcella's treachery and lies that warmed the seed of my eventual escape to Paris where I became known as Scarletta. This tag gave me some allure in the house of Lamont Couture, and in my *quartier* where I threw regular and extravagant parties. It was at one of these parties that I met Claude. He stayed behind after all the others had left. We sat and talked through the night, through my angst, until daylight lit the room. I knew that night that Paris was my home.

Marcella was smiling at her companions, who had arrived without my noticing. The late evening sun was replaced by the thudding of the rain, which after a steamy day was welcome. I ran my hand under my fringe, where beads of sweat had gathered. I tried to push away the dragging ghosts. Henri watching me said,

"You are a little lonely I think?"

He pursed his mouth to indicate his understanding.

"Yes! A little, but don't look so worried. I will behave myself tonight, I promise."

He turned his head to one side, frowning and I repeated,

"Promise, Henri! Really I will. I am going soon anyway."

I paid my tab then and waited. When Marcella and her two friends left, I followed. My eyes fastened on their heads and mouths. They were getting wet as rats. We were in the Marais area when they turned into a narrow, cobbled street with a high wall on one side. I knew this area well, as Claude's office had moved there in recent months. Their voices bounced around, like kites in the wind, and the click-clack of their shoes echoed. The entourage stopped at a heavy green door which opened into a courtyard. Inside the voices became muted, amidst the huge tree and sprawling vegetation made sweet and rank by the rain. They climbed the granite steps into one of the buildings. I had no plan in mind.

I walked into the courtyard as the mizzle grew softer and the cobblestones gave up globs of light from butter-coloured lamps. There was a familiar smell of cooking as I eased the door into the unlit hallway.

The tree's large branches threw shadows on the floor. Standing close to the full-length mirror, I smiled at myself, and patted my hair. Footsteps rushed down the stairs towards me and I hid in the lift with the out-of-order sign. Murmuring voices as a door opened. I stopped to look up from a corner on the first floor and heard,

"Okay Marcie! If you are sure you will be all right."

All doubts dispelled. It was Marcella. A shaft of pale light flooded the second floor landing from her open door. A television blared and muffled canned laughter was audible.

"Thanks for seeing me home."

Marcella's voice but without the hint of American. They kissed cheeks, amidst effuse goodbyes before passing me, where I stood, pretending to look for a key. The man said,

"She'll be all right. It was just one of those things."

Somewhere on the stairwell a cat protested as I continued my upward journey onto the darker landing of the fourth floor. I had a clear view of the spiralling stairway and sat and lit a cigarette. I needed to think this all out, to remember. She owed me an apology. That would be enough.

Marcella went to New York after she finished university from where filtered reports of her great successes came to me. Then at twenty-six she became engaged to a high society English photographer. She came back to Howth with him, to prepare for her nuptials and travelled around in a maroon-coloured Jaguar which her father gave her as an engagement present. As I got off the bus one day, she smiled at me through the car window, and the bile in the back of my throat almost suffocated me.

There was the big wedding in our village church. I remember sitting listening to the choir rehearse, the evening before. I had crept in through the half-open door and took the chair seat at the back which was half hidden by the statue of St Therese. There were no candles burning, no lumps of grease stuck here and there. Everything gleamed. I watched, the ladies whispering and laughing. Sometimes, little bursts of excitement caused their voices to rise.

"There will be TV cameras and all here tomorrow. It'll be the best wedding ever and no mistake. It will put Howth on the map alright. Everyone will be talking about it, pictures in the paper and all, and isn't she lovely?"

The voices lowered again. They filled the huge vases, tied little ribbons around the ends of the seats, rolled the red carpet down the aisle, cleaned and polished and swept. Then they saw me. They suggested politely that I should leave, saying that they were about to lock up the church. Outside I waited and found them out.

Marcella exited the church on the day in a cream silk dress, clinging to her handsome husband. All of her school friends were there; several invited back by her, from far off places. I stood alone, sharp with grief in the library doorway, glad that rain sluiced the village and hoping that all the wedding photos would be ruined.

The hallway was still but warmed by the purring of the cat, who rubbed himself against my legs. I lit another cigarette imagining myself calling at her door, insisting on talking to her.

"The truth," I would say, "Just admit the awful truth as your father said that day. The day my name was blackened by you. Just admit you are a barefaced liar to me. Just to me."

Tears backed up into my eyes. She had to repeat a year in Trinity College after what became known as the incident.

"So this is it. This is the awful truth of Marcella's poor grades. This is what she has been doing at your instigation. This is what you have brought her to," her father shouted at me the day of the big family meeting.

Marcella and I had just turned nineteen. She was in Trinity College and I was in the College of Art and Design. Marcella's spell over me had been firmly broken until, one day, we met by chance in the noisy bustle of Bewley's café in Grafton Street. I was surprised at her friendliness and dismayed at my need for her acknowledgement. Drawn in, I listened to the cadences of her voice as she moaned about her family, about some of her erstwhile friends and especially about her father's stinginess. She wondered if I had any ideas about how she might make some money for herself. Flattered, I suggested the Art College. Marcella became animated.

"A model? Me? In the nip and all? How much do they pay? Gosh!"

She was clearly titillated at the prospect. Before long she was the most sought after model on campus with her willowy looks and false but easy charm. My previous identity, so hard won, was swallowed up by her. I became known as Marcie's friend.

A buzzer sounded. I jumped as the hall filled with garish light. The stairs were mounted two by two. A man's tread. Eager. Marcella's door opened, folds of silk brushed against golden pumps. The pounding grew louder. Black patent shoes and the lower skirt of a dark duffle coat swayed, expectant.

"Marcie, cheri. You are okay?" His voice seductive and warm.

"Okay," she replied, pulling him to her and shutting the door. I imagined them then kissing in the narrow hallway, breathless half sentences and words mingling with their fumblings. I stood puzzling with some emotion that I couldn't quite hold.

"God!" I said to myself. What the hell are you doing hiding in the shadows, watching a thin line of light under a door? Are you going crazy? What would Claude think? Claude, who knew how to rescue me from the worst of myself. Claude, who will be home tomorrow, who will insist that we go to 'Le Pied du Cochon' where our knees will touch.

I ran down the stairs then. The tree swayed and seemed blurry in the semi-darkness. I wiped teardrops of rain from the wooden seat and sat for a moment, glad to have escaped. I lit another cigarette and savoured the taste. I knew where she was now I told myself, I could call back anytime. We needed to sort things out between us.

A mad gust of wind threw leaves and debris into the air, as I squashed the cigarette under my foot. I caught a handful of flower petals as they danced and folded my fingers around them without crushing them. I looked up to see Marcella by her open window, pert breasts pushing against her fluttering shirt. Pools of pain swamped me. Fall. Just fall, I thought, and felt a rush of hatred.

Her parents had called an urgent meeting of both families. My mother's look of shock and shame crushed me, as Marcella somehow made herself the victim of my scheming.

Mother said, "I blame myself, I do my best but she's never had a father, you see. He left before she was even born. Don't be too hard on her. She is not a bad girl, I know that."

Mr Edwards, red-faced, shouted at Mother then. She was close to tears. Then he swung around to where I sat, shaking.

"You were happy enough to allow our daughter sell her body and be leered at, but clever enough not to do it yourself."

"It wasn't like that," I tried to explain.

"I know my own daughter. She would never have done any of this except for your bad influence. My God! She is only a child still, and now we find out that she has had an abortion, organised and arranged for her by you."

He turned to Mother who was dabbing her eyes, and went on in his booming American voice.

"Organised by your daughter, against everything we believe in;

everything that Marcella knows to be dear and sacred. She will be scarred for life by this."

Somehow the drugs and condoms found in her room were my fault too. Marcella just sat there. It was an easy solution.

"You will never speak to her again. Do you understand? Not even hello. I hope I am making myself clear here." Mr Edwards said as we left .

"Pornographer!" they shouted at me in the village sometimes. "Dirty pornographer, that's what you are."

There were queer blots of colour in front of my eyes. The rising wind made the tree shudder and explode in confusion. Marcella laughed suddenly from the window above and the reverberations shook the walls. Was she looking down on me?

"Don't laugh at me," I hissed aloud "you liar! You bitch!"

Her lover came to her, like a shadow and kissed her face and mouth. I longed for Claude then, worse than longing. I needed to hear his voice saying,

"My fragile Scarletta," his French accent wobbling on fragile, "My favourite little pussycat."

Claude could always talk me round.

The tic-toc sound of the rain began to build. The lovers disappeared from view but Marcella's laugh once more echoed through the courtyard. I decided to leave. I needed to get away from her now. At the gate I turned to look at the glowing window. My fingers hooked around the enormous circular handle. Then I thought I heard Marcella's voice ricochet off the walls.

"Scarlett? Scarlett? Is that you?"

I stood frozen. The rain was in flux, unable to decide if it wanted to be a downpour or not. The wind too was full of contradictions, soft one minute and squally and turbulent the next.

"Scarlet? Scarlett? Is that you?"

I stepped back inside and re-took my seat under the tree. The gutters trickled and sang at the sullen building. The window was empty now, the light dimmed. A long time I sat there. Then I went back in.

The door opened like a dark tongue into the hall. The mirror held some shivering light, and I smiled at my shadowy reflection. I climbed the stairs once more but let the pink petals fall from my hand, through the railings. One stuck to the palm of my hand and I picked it clean away. The petals quivered and floated; some stuck to the railings momentarily, before falling onto the cold tiles. I stood and watched, leaning right over until every single stupid petal lay on the floor below. I heard mumbled sounds from behind Marcella's door as I turned away, to knock and press the buzzer at the same time.

"Marcella?" She stood in front of me without shoes, her blouse haphazardly buttoned.

"Yes! Can I help you?"

She was different, younger and her eyes were deep set and brown.

"Marcella Edwards?"

"Marcella Cleary." She replied with an anxious turn of her head.

Of course, she was married, but that wasn't it.

"Do I know you?" She placed the door in front of herself protectively.

"No! I thought... Someone called. I mean I was looking for Marcella. You're from Dublin? It's just that I am from Dublin, you see.'"

"I'm from Cork actually."

She looked at me with pitying eyes.

"What a strange coincidence. There must be some mix-up I suppose," she said.

Marcella smiled then, revealing crooked teeth which made her disarmingly attractive.

The light in the hallway where I stood, snapped off and plunged us into darkness, except for the warm brightly lit apartment which framed her. I was delirious. Emotions rushed through me like a flame. She was not Marcella Edwards at all. She couldn't interfere in my life ever again.

"Oh! Look! I'm sorry, my mistake. Some mix-up like you said."

She might ask me in. We could become friends.

"That's all right." She smiled again. "I hope you find whoever you are looking for."

"I hope I never do." I said as I gripped the curling stairway, dizzy with happiness. My fingers danced against the rail. I pressed myself into the wall as their voices melded together again. The door thudded shut. The cat once more brushed against my legs and ran onto the landing, to claw Marcella's door, mewling.

"Come on kitty. Be a good pussy cat." I heard her voice again.

There was nothing American about it at all. From the open door, a slit of light cut into the darkness and the man spoke. The cat slunk in past his legs still crying. The man looked down into the darkened stairwell. The door clicked shut.

I began to walk down the stairs, fingers coiling around the handrail. As I approached the door I noticed the woman in the mirror, crying, mascara smudges on her cheeks. I touched the mirrors as if to wipe away the tears, my mind empty. The mouth was working. There was no sound just the mouth. I watched and tried to understand.

"Come in here, you silly pussycat. Yes! Yes! That's right you are my favourite pussycat." The man at Marcella's door had said.

"Claude? Claude?" I said aloud.

Then I smashed my fist into the mirror, and all my demons grinned.

Back in the Days

Nomleth Nyapokoto

Back in the days, grandfathers loved and trusted,
Grandmothers remained strong and faithful,
Old men left their families behind.

They travelled to seek for jobs in the cities.
Nowadays mothers don't allow dads
To work in a faraway land.
Back in the days, grandfathers loved and trusted.

Once they leave to work away, the unity shatters.
These days trust is musk worn by our dads.
Old men left their families behind.

In the olden days trust was their daily bread.
In these days, you'd rather trust a stone than a person.
Back in the days, grandfathers loved and trusted.

Grandfathers left and came back.
Dads leave and never come back.
Old men left their families behind.

Grandmothers were faithful and hopeful.
Mothers are hopeless and faithless.
Back in the days, fathers loved and trusted.
Old men left their families behind.

Debt

Marcella Morgan

The singing lady stood on tiptoe in the centre of a field in the centre of a city. The field was a park but it was a new park and so it looked more like a field. It had a few thin trees dressed in raggy leaves and a lonely bench on the top of a gentle rise that hid the raw flowerbeds from view. People walked their dogs.

For years and years the lady did not touch the earth. She moved around her home by jumping from one piece of furniture to another. Dinner was prepared by squatting on the kitchen counter with her legs spread and her hands busy between them chopping vegetables, kneading bread and rolling pastry. Outside she only walked on walls. She climbed buildings sideways. She walked along the roofs of cars.

One day, a man who called himself a friend asked her why she behaved the way she did. She said to him, "If I touch the earth then I owe it my weight and I do not want to be in debt to the earth." The man sighed and said, "If I lie in a bed I owe it my weight. While it owes the earth its weight and mine and yours if you slept in the bed with me. If you lie on me, you owe me. You are in debt to every object which bears your weight."

From that day on she would only stand or sit or lie on the earth. She did not use furniture and she dug up the floors of her house to expose the dirt underneath. When she left her house she leapt from one oasis of earth to another. She wore a jackhammer over her shoulder. She hammered out a path through tarmac for herself, screamed and ripped at the floor of the prisons they put her in, leaving her nails behind her when she walked free to be faced with a concrete parking lot which she ran over screaming like an unprepared hot coal walker. This happened regularly.

She began to walk on tiptoe but the man who called himself a friend explained that although she had decreased the area of her body touching the earth by standing in this way, the amount of pressure she was putting on the earth had not decreased. It had merely intensified.

She began to starve herself. She ate an apple a day. At eight fifteen every morning she ate her apple. It took her one hour to eat it. She peeled it first and then she put the whole fruit in her mouth and she sucked it dry. Then she took it out of her mouth and stretched her mouth and moved her jaw over and back and then she cut the apple into triangular pieces and ate them. Then she gathered the skin pieces together and scraped the flesh from them with her teeth and then she chewed on the skin until it was mush and then she took the mush from her mouth and rolled it into little balls and she tossed them in the air and caught them in her mouth and swallowed them. She became very thin.

One day the man who called himself a friend died and she stood beside his grave and watched as the earth swallowed him and then she walked on tiptoe from the graveyard to the centre of the park that looks like a field. She wore grey. From the tip of her toes the grey arched up her legs to the wide flat of her pelvis and curved on up to her stomach until it reached the tip of her breasts. From this apex, the grey rolled down over the ridges of her upside-down head and then suddenly down her stiff arms to her finger points. She began to sing.

And then with her song come to an end, the lady un-curved. She stood pencil straight on the tip of her toes. She took a bottle of fuel that she had brought with her and she unscrewed the top with long and delicate fingers. She lifted it above her head thrown back as if to receive a drop of rain. She poured the contents over her body.

She lit a match. It flared on the first strike. She held it before her and slowly she brought it closer to her chest and closer still until her hand was pressed against her chest hard. The flame licked the underside of her chin, exploded in flames and the rest of her body followed screaming. She was surprised, she was shocked by it.

The flames twirled her round and round she pirouetted with red orange grey ribbons so fast she was lifted from the ground higher and higher she spun burning into the air until she was in the air was the air was nothing nothing on earth nothing owing nothing owed.

Somewhere

Samantha McCaffrey

"I always feel empty and sad"
He said, "After"
As he came out of me.
He looked washed away from me,
On the shoreline of my bed.

"I know" I said.
I did.

I saw him then
Small
This runaway boy,
Shivering and lost,
Crowned by an empty shed
Somewhere in an Irish field,
While circling all around
Local people scurried,
Searching.

Lost is a pattern
Ridged like an Irish field.

God's Gardener

Conn Redmond

It's funny that I, of all people, should find myself standing at a window overlooking Dublin's Garden of Remembrance.

Maybe if I stare long enough all of the memories I've already lost will grow back again, just like the newly sprouted flowers in this garden that remembers.

What will become of everything I'll lose over the coming days and months? Where will my life go to? Will God's gardener rake up my memories and toss them away or gather a mound and with a flame set light to everything I've known? Ashes to ashes, scattered and windblown, falling on people in tiny specks as they pass. A minute jigsaw puzzle assembled on shoulders and heads and carried to the four corners of the city.

I feel so much part of this place it would be a fitting gift: everything I've ever known and loved.

The view from the window is misted from my exhaled breath – the back of my hand brings it all slowly back, skin feeling damp and cold suddenly as the view reappears in my eyes. Oh, how I wish it could be that easy, when every time something precious is disappearing you could wipe your hand against some invisible window and it all slowly and magically returns.

Maybe they were all wrong, those experts in the field, maybe, hopefully.

I close my eyes, lids heavy, chase flickers of recall; they appear waif-like and mischievous.

My own face as a child, my Dad's carpenter's hands chipped and scarred, my brother falling from his bike crying and holding a cut knee and hobbling to the back door of our house. A kitchen radio playing loudly, a net curtain blowing softly at an open window. Sand between my toes and a child's half filled bucket of seawater, a tiny crab trying to climb up the inside and sliding back again and again, two small faces reflected in the water, eyes wide in fascination.

The Angelus bell at six, the man who worked the field at the end of the road passing five minutes after, his black bike squeaks past, I see him, a bunch of leeks hanging limply from his overcoat pocket.

A kettle whistles. No, it's a train; a man is too close to the edge of the platform. He steps back in time.

Back I go; everything I've known.

The woman who kept clocks, a room of full of ticking, I'd deliver milk and bread, biscuits and tea bags from the shop up the road and she'd say how wonderful I was.

Running with my dog, me out of puff and he's lost to me as he chases the waves and darts back again and runs and runs. I walk holding a lead he doesn't want. I'd hate it if something happened to him.

Something did happen to him. My eyes dart open. The light is falling quietly. The large room is empty; its high white ceiling, large windows and heavy red curtains still open to the day. I walk along each one and pull the drawstring, the last one not fully closing leaving a small gap my hand makes larger, revealing a city disappearing slowly to a late December afternoon.

The streetlights blink, a pale yellow at first, cars pass, dots of rain. A footstep falls on the squeaky staircase outside. I let the curtain fall back. I can see a light under the door.

It's the woman coming to lock up. She wants to know if anybody is there.

"I'm here," and then louder but she's gone.

It's time to trace my way home.

The banisters help me down passing haunted paintings hung like obituaries.

Outside in the cold air, which way? Buttoning my coat I take a left and see a fire burning, a curtain drawing the night away. The rain is heavier and where is my umbrella? I walk back to the heavy door and knock but nobody answers. Looking up I see a dim light at the top of the building. Maybe I didn't bring my umbrella. I don't knock again and walk to a bus stop, drips of cold rain spotting my coat, small puddles forming in the potholes I step over to get to the other side of the road. A car stops suddenly and blows its horn; I thought the light was green for me. The driver gesticulates wildly and my heart races.

There are too many people, Christmas lights blur in shop windows close to my bus stop, this one here, is it this one? Why do my legs shake so? I lean close to a wall for shelter. A young woman offers a share of her umbrella. We stand and wait and she talks but I can't talk back and I feel choked and alone. I close my eyes and think, think hard, take my mind away.

I'm lying on flattened grass beside the beach, a blue sky, and hands behind my back, uncaring. A warm breeze wafts across my face.

The umbrella flaps closed and I step on to a bus, the woman looking at me, almost maternal, talking, reassuring as a young man gets up from his seat and I sit beside a fogged-over window.

With my index finger I make a small round shape on the wet glass and peep through. Sometimes familiar places jolt my sense memory along the way.

I see a café – stained glass windows it used to have. As a young woman I'd sit there with friends or alone with a steaming cup and a book. The tall coloured windows seemed to capture the light from outside and hold it magically. A fireplace lay at one corner of the room, red embers. Old men wearing dark suits would sit around it and murmur to each other through a blue haze of pipe tobacco.

And oh, that shop just passed, a tear spurts from my eye. I bought my wedding gown there, so long ago. He had such a head of dark hair and smiling eyes I'd never seen before. He was so nervous asking me. So lucky to have found each other in this big world. A world that grew cold after he'd passed, even a spring day, walks with my grandchildren, time spent with friends, were all missing him.

I went back there today, to the place he used to work, that old Georgian building, those large rooms, just to stand and feel for his presence, to walk the old wood stairs and along the narrow corridors.

I may not be able to find it again, the next time. We'd meet for summer lunchtime picnics in the Garden of Remembrance, we'd sit on a seat quietly eating and would brush crumbs off each other as he stood to return to work.

He was tall and well groomed, always neat, clean and polished shoes. I'd watch him walk away and sometimes I wondered if we were still happy together, but he'd always turn to look back at me just before the gate.

The bus has left the city behind and streets of houses appear. A boarded-up corner shop passes and this is where I should get off. I finger the inside of my coat pocket for my door keys but find only a handkerchief. I push my other hand nervously into the other and feel the cold metal jingle.

The rain has stopped. Most of the people have already left the bus.

I step through the late evening and along a wet footpath to my door. The hallway frightens me in darkness for a moment until the hall light illuminates paintings along the wall and a wooden coat stand, an umbrella lying at its feet.

The grate in the drawing room is set and ready for lighting. I scratch a red match from a large box on the mantelpiece and watch the dry sticks take hold, crackle and burn brightly. A shake of coal and it smokes enough to know that I will soon be warm again.

A towel to dry my hair, a cup of tea and the day recedes quickly, a cosy armchair pulled close. Such a big room, so hard to heat now. Our piano lies gracefully in one corner, old wood furniture and picture frames filled with smiling faces that look over me.

I take a seat and open the cover. All those keys. I flick through music and lay my hands down. They start to play, Chopin, waltz in A minor.

I reach the end of the sheet. I remembered every chord.

The fire is red. My chair sits opposite his. I stir the embers with a crooked poker and wait.

The life I've lived will keep me company, the memory of music, strong tea, and these warm toes. I'll wait. Until the sun comes up again over that garden that remembers.

Je Suis Pierre

Orla Ní Chuilleanain

"Je suis Pierre," said a four-year-old, in a carriage of sweat and fear.

His pink cheeks were hot and rounded, his elbows bent, as the slippery palm of one hand felt for the slippery palm of the other hand at his tubby waist.

"Je suis Pierre," he said, again and again, looking up at the gaunt chins of passengers, dead-eyed or wet-eyed, already grieving. He spoke as though this little nugget of important information – all he had, in fact – would make the train stop, his self be recognised, everything explained. A vital introduction from an unconditional world.

The stars outside were cold. It was not enough to have neat little fingers, a brain feeling regular flickers of light on the retina. The dead who had once caressed him, fed him and clothed him, loved him from the first, had left only a name. "Je suis Pierre," he said.

Perhaps at last, he said it only to himself. Fog on the brains and hearts that did it. The shadows are their own nightmare. His heart beat like any other heart, but then it stopped. And where he fell, limp-limbed and lung-filled, in a tangle of heads and legs, no words lived.

Days in Time
Paul O'Regan

He had been looking forward to this all year, a last birthday present to himself. He'd promised his wife before she died that he would go, that he would not put it off any longer. She knew how important this was to him, knew that he had to do this even though it would kill him. Not to do it could make so much simply disappear.

He glanced through the forms again and signed them. His hand shook, his signature wavering on the screen, but it scanned OK, the computer recognising him. The process now complete, he relaxed a little. Soon he would see if he was right. Either way he would see his Rose again.

He stood, pulled on his jacket and headed for the door. Taking in the state of his house, the notes addressed to his children stacked neatly on the desk monitor, flat against the black marble table. Various lights flickered throughout the house, the red eye lights of modern technology looking after things. A TV discreetly inlaid in a picture frame, a micro-stereo in a plant stand – good for the plants apparently. Pulling the door closed behind him he stepped into the waiting taxi.

"Days in Time offices please, out on Ventura, you know it?"

"Yeah, been there a couple of times," replied the cabby. "You work there?"

"I used to."

"I've been meaning to give it a go, that time-travelling thing, sounds kinda fun. You ever try it?"

"Once or twice."

"I'm not too old am I? I heard something about you having to be young or something?"

"You do. You look like you'd be OK. You should go. It really is all that they say about it."

The conversation drifted along with the traffic. Each cab ride was another chance to retell the dog-eared stories of his youth. By the time they had arrived the taxi driver was shaking his head

"You certainly were a lively one alright, sir. If even half those stories are true you're a braver man then me."

Stepping into the office he was greeted by the CEO, a man who had made his considerable fortune from him, from one of those unbelievable stories.

200

"Kieran, how are you. I know we've been over this, but I would like you to hear me out."

"Now James, as you said, we've been over this. My mind is made up."

The CEO, giving up, walked silently with his mentor. He had been paid handsomely for his part in what was happening, but it hurt him that his friend had come here to die.

Running through the formalities, Kieran donned his flight suit. It still fit him after all these years. Though the process had become mainstream now: families travelling back in time to witness the day of the dinosaurs or the first flight by the Wright brothers, he thought he would travel in the way he had when he pioneered the science: in his test flight gear. Stepping into the chamber he dialled in his destination and schedule. Dublin, Ireland, 1979. Sitting back into the neat fitting seat, he pulled the door closed and pressed the ignition.

Around him the walls of the craft flickered from red to white. Translucent to black, orange to blue. He could feel his heart pounding against the strain, but he was not worried, he knew this would work, this part at least. As a wind blew through the cockpit, a drop of blood slipped from his ear, landing unseen on his shoulder.

Then the wind stopped. The colours stopped. His heart pounded in his ears. All around him the sights and sounds of his youth hammered at him. He had landed in a park in the summer time, full of families walking and running. Unseen he pulled open the door of the craft. People walked past him, around him, through him. He wasn't there. He knew this, had experienced it many times before, but it still made him feel strange.

He walked with the crowd now. It was a hot summer's day, and though he was not really there, he swore that he could feel the heat of the sun. He could not remember the popular style of the time he grew up, but all around him, the bright colours of the seventies blasted at his memory. The long hair, the baggy clothes, mothers with hair bands, teenage boys with wide leather wrist watches, all so very old, so familiar, so much like home. And then he saw them.

His mother! Her hair, it was so blonde and she was so young. Much younger then he was now. And that boy, that tall thin boy looking over his mother's shoulder, that must be Colm. His brother. My God, he was so tall, so strong. The last time he had seen his brother he was a shell, shrivelled from the cancer that had killed him. That had been almost thirty years before. The tears tumbled down his face, his heart wrenching harder now.

Lying on the grass, staring at the crowds around them were two kids, a boy and a girl of about six or seven. He hardly recognised Rose or himself, two kids that had sworn friendship forever. His arm began to ache, he knew his heart was about to give out, but that did not scare him. He had done the right thing, just a little more time and he would know for certain. And after that, well… he missed his Rose more than anything in the world. It wouldn't be long now.

He could not hear what the kids were saying but somewhere in his mind a far off memory was making itself heard. I remember the man, the old man crying.

With that the boy turned and looked straight at Kieran. The boy smiled and went to wave at the see-through man but as he waved the man began to dissolve, his body fading and disappearing in the wind.

For years afterwards the boy would remember that old man, not knowing why, but always wondering about him. As the boy grew to become a man he studied engineering and literature. As his classmates and workmates created buildings and software, he created stories of new worlds and fantastic inventions. One morning he stood shaving: the mirror slightly misted over, when he glimpsed a ghost. A reflection of that old man from the park, the old man that he would become. In that instant of connection he thought of the past. And of the future, and a way of connecting the two.

The Scar

V.B. Reid

John has never seen a dead body. But he remembers seeing one.

When he was a child there was a fire in the local haberdashery shop and when the fire was put out, the charred naked mannequin in the window left a scar on his brain that never went away. He never spoke of it then nor in the intervening years but he thought about it from time to time. Each of those times the scar grew. It became something more, some bigger experience. The mannequin became a person. Then it became someone he knew.

For a time it was the shop owner. He was a tall, bald man, a friend of the family. He had a laugh like sunshine. Whenever they went into the shop he would try to steal John's nose.

Then it was a friend of John's. His best friend who had gone in with the measurements for their front room curtains. His wife had nagged him so. He kept forgetting, or he was putting it off for some reason. The shopkeeper's son had taken over the business and John's friend didn't like him. They had been at school together and there had been some fight between them over some girl. There was bad blood. He had only been in the shop for a minute when the fire broke out. He had just popped in for a minute.

John never married. If he had married he might have told his wife about the dead mannequin. How it came into his dreams at night. How it worried him. She might have remembered for him that it was just a mannequin. Yes it looked like a burned corpse but it had never been a living thing. There was no need to worry, no need to be afraid.

But he never married. And the scar kept growing.

When John thought of his father it would bring tears to his eyes. How he saved all those women in the shop. How he had carried them out one by one over his shoulder. How he went back in for the shopkeeper even though he didn't like him. They had been in school together and there had been a fight over a girl. Marjorie he thought her name was. There had been bad blood ever since. Then he would remember how the firemen had carried his father's charred body out after the fire had been quenched. It had taken two of them to lift him. John's father was a giant of a man, a gentle man, and a gentleman. He had lost his life trying to save a man he didn't care for.

"Mr Smith. Mr Smith. Would you like a cup of tea?" the voice says.

It's the older nurse, the plain one. She smiles a lot. John knows it isn't real smiling though. She talks through her teeth like she was on Miss World.

John says he would like a cup of tea, please.

She asks him how is he feeling, if it hurts. He knows that she knows he doesn't understand. He doesn't say anything and then she gestures towards his leg. He looks down and sees that it's in a cast. He looks back to the nurse. It's the plain one, the older one. She is smiling.

"We'll get you a nice cup of tea," she says.

John drops off after his tea. He has a dream about his brother. The time they tried to make candles in the big kitchen in the old house. They were melting the wax on the big stove. The temperature was too high, or there was something in the wax that shouldn't have been there and it caught fire. It blew up. They put it out with a wet towel but part of the ceiling was black and ruined. Their mother was very angry but their father wasn't. He acted like he was but John knew he was only pretending. He was amused that they had done something a bit stupid. He was trying not to laugh. He had to in front of their mother. She was so stern and so strict with them. The punishment was they had to clean and repaint the ceiling. The whole ceiling mind, not just the part that was black and ruined.

When he wakes up he doesn't remember the dream. He doesn't remember the brother. The man in the bed beside him is sleeping. His snoring has no rhyme or reason to it. It comes and goes like that jazz music that his mother used to like.

There is another nurse here now. Or she could be a doctor, John thinks. They have women doctors now.

She keeps saying, "Hello Mr Smith". She says it nice but John doesn't know how he's supposed to respond. So he says nothing. Then he thinks she's a head doctor, and this is some sort of test. He wants to acknowledge that he understands what's happening but she's already writing something on a pad.

She looks up when she's done writing.

"Mr Smith", she says. "Do you remember yesterday?"

John says, "What happened yesterday?" He didn't mean to say it. He meant to think about it first or to say, yes of course, and then think about it.

"You fell, don't you remember?"

John thinks about it. He is sore alright but then he often is. He is straining on it, urging his brain to move faster.

"You fell and you broke your leg, I'm afraid. Do you remember Nurse Bently put a cast on it for you?"

He says, yes of course, but the woman is looking at him with something like pity he thinks. He wants to tell her something. Her eyes have opened wider like she's expecting him to say something. She reminds him of his school teacher. Mrs Bently her name was. Marjorie Bently. She was always so kind to him. The time she buttoned up his jacket for him when he was waiting outside the school for his mother to come and pick him up, to keep him warm. Then he remembers the fire. All the people outside the shop. His mother putting her hands over his eyes and turning him towards her so that he wouldn't see. But he did see. He saw Mrs Bently in the window.

He saw her. He saw her hair had all been burned off and she was screaming.

He looks up and he thinks he's ready to tell her about the scar on his brain that keeps growing and growing. But his mother has gone.

After dinner John is listening to the man in the bed next to him. He is talking about the war. He was a soldier and he had fought in the war. His childhood love had married because word had got to her that he had died. A body had been sent home. It was all burned and they thought it was him but it wasn't him. When the war was over he got his discharge papers and he went home to marry her. He had proposed to her before the war and she had said yes. His mother had to break the news to him that Marjorie had married the man from the haberdashery shop and they were expecting their first child.

John wakes up in the night. He knows it's the night because there is a light at the next bed. Apart from that it is all dark. John knows that the man in the next bed has died. They are cleaning him, he thinks, and then they are dressing him.

It makes him think of when his mother died. How he never saw her. How it was a closed casket because of the burns. She was such a warm person, such a lovely mother, so kind and loving. It pains him so that the last image of her in his head was that woman in the window of the haberdashery shop. That charred body with no hair. That thing that had once been a living thing but now it wasn't. It wasn't his mother anymore. The truth is, the way it looked it could almost have just been a mannequin.

John falls back to sleep. And then his mother is there, holding him close. She says that there is no need to worry, no need to be afraid.

Périphérique.
M.M. Cotter

You know that it is not working. You do not discuss this. Instead, you book a 'romantic weekend break', on the cheap. Paris, or rather Paris Beauvais. This is the first mistake in an attempt to breathe life into this death rattle of a relationship. Coping with the bus from Beauvais to Paris (Paris Paris, you think, as opposed to Paris Beauvais), stuck in a traffic jam for over an hour, is not a good start. Your fellow bus passengers have facial tics, body odour, stammers, wind. They are not conducive to reviving romance.

Eventually, you reach the hotel. It is not at all how you expected it to be. The bedroom is small and dark, and the noise from the street is deafening. The en-suite bathroom is smaller than the toilet on the airplane. It seems necessary to engage in some sort of physical congress on arrival, though. After all, it is Paris.

Afterwards, after a cold shower (no hot water), you are ready for the next mission. Dinner in Paris. Unafraid of new experiences in *cuisine*, you order the steak tartare. You are aware that this is raw meat. But you were not expecting it to be raw meat with raw egg and some peas or something (capers, you learn later). This is disgusting, you think. Surely there must be some mistake. You are disappointed. The waiter takes away your barely touched plate, with obvious disdain. You are not a Parisienne.

The following day, shopping in Les Galeries Lafayette, your non-Parisienneness is again driven home. French women are stick insects. You are a behemoth. You realise that they do not eat *crêpes* with chocolate and banana two hours after a croissant with butter and a hot chocolate. They have had black coffee and cigarettes. You resolve to start smoking again, for a week or two anyway. Dissatisfied with your own appearance, your thoughts turn to your companion on this weekend of *l'amour*. Dispassionately, you catalogue his faults. He catches you looking at him. You have been thinking, "I hate the way his eyebrows meet in the middle". You do not say this. You smile. He smiles. You both look away.

Dinner that evening. Conversation is stilted. You think of finishing the relationship there and then. Over coffee, you imagine your reaction to his death, by accidental drowning in the Seine, for example. You would be genuinely sad, undoubtedly. And in a rush of genuine sadness, you defer your termination of the relationship – time enough when you get back. You walk along the banks of the Seine together. You are holding hands and smiling. At no point does he look like falling into the river and drowning accidentally. In any case, you wouldn't wish it on his parents, to lose a son at an early age. You are magnanimous in your not wishing him dead. It is your last night in Paris.

Back at the hotel, after the obligatory sex (Paris, remember – you can't not do it), you stare at the dark ceiling. You consider your options. He is not an evil man. You do not want to be alone. Once more, you defer making any decisions.

The week after you come back, you discuss with your girlfriends over many bottles of wine the pros and cons of staying in this relationship with him. The romance is dissected, compared and contrasted to others. The alternatives are weighed up. His good points are reiterated. The combined opinion favours continuing the liaison. The received wisdom is that all couples go through phases of boredom, of stagnation, of wondering. The crucial thing is, on balance, you love each other, they decide. Your girlfriends advocate frank discussions, openness, addressing the issues that you have been skirting and circling. You are reminded of Paris, a childhood holiday this time. The family had come over on the car ferry, in the family car, with the IRL sticker declaring your nationality. Somehow, your father had got stuck on the Périphérique, the ring road that circles the city. The right-hand-drive car was in the middle of eight lanes of aggressive Parisian drivers, and your father had twice missed the exit he wished to take off the motorway. Committed to once again driving the whole way around the twenty-odd miles to reach the exit, it seemed that you would never be able to get off the ring road, and that you were destined to spend the rest of the holiday circling around Paris, until the traffic died down in the dead of night or the car ran out of petrol. You resolve to stop skirting around important decisions in your life.

Coming home, buoyed up and optimistic about your future as a couple, you find that the object of your affection and discussions is still awake despite the late hour. "You know that everything is going to work out okay; all couples have these 'patches.'" He says, "we need to talk." "Darling," you say, "I know, I've just been thinking the same thing." He says, "I've met someone else… "

This is not what was meant to happen. You think, why couldn't he have drowned?

A Reluctant Renaissance

Marian Redmond

Nessa was dreaming. This time she was telling Joe that he was being made redundant and that she would look after him. He was crying and holding onto her knees, begging her to reconsider. Then she woke up. The sun was streaming into the bedroom. It took her a few moments before she realised where she was. She realised that she'd slept all the way through the evening. She jumped out of bed, feeling stupid. Had she really been that exhausted. Her dreams had been so vivid. She had dreamed that she held Joe's fate in her hands and was luxuriating in the feeling. But that's all it was, a dream. She actually felt disappointed. It would have been so nice to have had that kind of power over Joe. But she hadn't. He had wielded his corporate power over her and so here she was, in a modest pensione on the Amalfi coast, supposedly healing her soul and thus readying herself for the return to Dublin and the quest for a new job.

This morning she didn't feel she had the strength to do anything except have a strong expresso and wander around the town. She quickly got herself ready and went down to a lovely smell that was wafting itself up the stairs. The smell of freshly baked rolls and freshly brewed coffee. There was no one in the dining room. She felt strong enough to pop her head through the kitchen door to bid good morning to Signora Rosa or Rosa as she quickly corrected herself. She barely held the door open as she said the words. She felt embarrassed about sleeping all the way through dinner the previous evening. She deliberately tried to make her voice sound light and sweet although she didn't feel particularly so right now.

"Buon giorgno, Rosa,"

There was no reply. Rosa was busy. Perhaps it was better not to intrude too much into Rosa's kitchen so soon. The last thing she wanted to appear was presumptuous and pushy. There was no one else in the dining room. She'd sit there.

The weight of her bad dreams still hung over her. She sat at a small table near the window. She'd look out at the morning in a few minutes, after her coffee. She sat down and sighed heavily, feeling the weight of the last few months hanging over her.

"Buon giorgno, Signora,"

A deep male voice spoke to her and she found herself looking into two amused hazel-coloured eyes. This had to be Massimo, the busy son. He was about thirty-years-old, she estimated, and quite attractive. Very attractive, in fact. He had the kind of black, floppy hair that seemed to be a prerequisite for the leading man in an Italian film. He had brilliant white teeth. Graham's teeth had been crooked and they had depressed her when he smiled, which was rarely. Joe's teeth had started off white but had disimproved over the years. She used to have to make his dental appointments for him. Why was she thinking about them now? She was supposed to be getting away from all of those memories here.

"How are long are you staying in Maoiri, Signora?" Massimo asked as he poured her freshly made coffee from a large pot. It smelt strong and good.

So his English was as good as his mother's, if not better.

"I'm not entirely sure. A few weeks, maybe longer."

He looked puzzled. He was probably so used to the package holidaymakers with their tight one and two-week schedules. She didn't have to explain but she wanted to.

"I used to work in Dublin and they got rid of me suddenly. So I've come here to relax and plan what I'm going to do with the rest of my life."

It sounded so empty and lifeless but Massimo had nodded as she spoke.

"The same thing happened to my uncle and aunt. They worked together for thirty years in a factory in Naples and then suddenly it went bust and they were left high and dry. But they came home here and set up their own business just like Mama. Now they are happier than they ever dreamed of before. Maybe the same thing will happen to you, Signora."

Nessa nodded and smiled. But inside she felt barren. Barren of ideas and barren of hope. What chance would she ever have of being happy again. Happier. That meant she was happy at some time in the past. Was she ever happy? Not since she was starting college, filled with excitement at the whole academic world and the possibilities that seemed to be there for her. She had dreamed of being an archaeologist. But that hadn't happened, had it. Graham had happened and all of her dreams had evaporated. She had thought she was all right, working and keeping everything going. Then Joe had blown all of that away.

"You have to ask yourself, Senora, what are you interested in? What sets you on fire? What makes your blood burn? Then you have to go after it and grasp it."

He smiled broadly at her. Surely he wasn't flirting with her? She could feel herself responding to him, despite a little voice inside her saying 'don't be a fool".

"Well, I used to love ancient history. I studied it at university. I am going to visit all of the ancient places now that I am here."

"But this is great news. I sometimes help a friend of mine out. He works as a private guide to wealthy American tourists who want to visit the archaeological sites during the quieter seasons and who want individual guides. I take some of his smaller groups. You must accompany me on one of them."

"Well, that's very kind of you. I was going to visit as many of the ancient sites as I could. Thank you."

Well, that explained why his English was so good. Nessa smiled and this time, probably for the first time since she had arrived, if she was truly honest with herself, her smile was genuine and not forced. She did intend to go to all of the places that she had studied and dreamed about when she was young. But she was dreading booking trips on the big tourist buses with their regimented timetables and their insistence on bland humour on the journeys. How would she have fitted in there? She imagined that her palpitations would return.

"Well, enjoy your day, Signora."

She thanked him again and smiled again. He really was quite attractive. His muscles rippled under his white tee-shirt. She shook her head. She was being quite stupid. The first day I'm here, I start to think about the first Italian man I meet. How clichéd I am. She turned and looked out of the window near her. She could see the sun, already bright and glowing with bright light at nine in the morning. The sight of it cheered her up and she finished her coffee looking out across the sea at its golden reflection on the waves. The coffee was really good. She was beginning to enjoy her day.

After breakfast, she got her bag from her room and walked towards the front door, meeting Rosa on the way. She wasn't quite as friendly as last night. Nessa couldn't think why but guessed it was because she had missed dinner.

"Good morning, Signora Nessa. You are well today? I hear that you met Massimo."

"Yes, I am well, thank you. And yes, I did meet your son. He gave me some really good coffee and we talked."

"Yes, he told me. He said that you might be going on one of his private tours to Pompeii or Herculaneum."

Nessa thought that she heard some disapproval in Rosa's voice. She decided to ignore it.

"Yes, he said I could come along. It is very kind of him. I will pay, of course."

"Of course."

Rosa definitely sounded annoyed by this. Perhaps it was to be expected. She didn't want her son to be exploited by some tourist looking for a free trip. It must be an Italian mother thing, this protectiveness.

"I was just going to walk around the town before it gets too hot, Rosa. I will see you later."

She made sure to give her a big, open smile as she walked past. The very last thing she needed right now was hassle with Rosa. She'd come here to get away from hassle, not walk into more. She stepped out into the brightness and began to descend the steps that had almost defeated her last night. It was so much easier to go down than up. This thought amused her as she remembered why she was here and she laughed out loud, startling a woman who was passing her by on her way up. Well, she'd certainly gone down in the world recently but had it been easy?

She walked down the hill towards the seafront promenade, feeling like a charlatan. She sat on a bench and tried to calm herself down. She didn't really have a life now. But she had to make one. And the whole point of her being here was to decide how she was going to do it. What she was feeling now was anger. She thought of all the things she had done for Joe. Taking his calls, making his tea, covering up for him. Every day of her life in that office and it had all meant nothing in the end. She clenched her fists. She just had to stop this. Was Joe thinking about her now? No, he was probably thinking about Rosaleen. She had to try to think about the future, not the past. But they were intertwined, weren't they. She was the product of her past. Her newly acquired panic attacks were testament to that. She heard a giggle and looked around. A woman with two young children was walking past staring at her and her children were giggling at her. She realised that she had been clenching her fists for at least five minutes and she must have been groaning aloud as she thought about Joe. She made an effort to smile and picked herself up off the bench, deciding that it was time to decide what exactly she was going to do today.

She realised that she'd passed the church with the fresco as she'd walked down to the promenade without it even registering consciously, deep inside her own angry memories. Maybe it was time to start looking for spiritual peace. Where better for an Irish ex-catholic like herself to start than a church? She made her way back up to the fresco and stood looking at it properly. It was definitely not old. Something about the style and the colours made her think it had been painted in the nineteen fifties. The seafront looked completely different from what she could remember of her brief time last night when she had arrived there. She decided to go in to the church. It looked cool and inviting.

Inside, she walked around, savouring the inside of an Italian church. The last time she'd been in one was when Graham and her had made a disastrous trip to the Vatican.

It had been a blisteringly hot day in Rome and they'd had to queue for two hours to get in. Then the interior was filled with Japanese tourists, talking loudly and pointing at everything. They also insisted on taking pictures, much to the annoyance of the guides and the security men, who followed them around, shaking their fists at them.

Graham had been speechless with annoyance at this desecration. He had insisted on leaving, before she'd had a chance to look at anything properly. They'd had a row outside, much to the amusement of the queuing tourists. She'd stormed off, not returning to their hotel for hours.

Well, this time she was going to take her time and have a proper look, even if this wasn't the Vatican but only a small church in a coastal town. She stood and looked at all the statues and the paintings on the walls. She walked up to the altar and stood, looking at an elaborately cased shrine, observing that it was as if time had stood still and she was back in the church she'd gone to as a child. Nothing had been modernised here. The colours, the atmosphere were what she remembered from her Catholic childhood. She sat in one of the dark wooden pews that smelt of polish. She even found herself saying a prayer. She prayed that she would find some peace of mind here and return to Dublin, refreshed and ready for whatever lay ahead. She heard a noise behind her. It was the priest, checking the church. He smiled at her and went back into his office at the side. She followed him and found him sitting at his desk. She muttered 'Grazie' and 'Bella' at him, motioning to the church. He nodded. He didn't speak English. This almost surprised her after her experience in the *pensione*. Feeling embarrassed, she fumbled in her bag and put a ten euro note in the offerings box she'd noticed on the way in and walked back out into the sunshine.

Then it was down the steps to the town, this time of the morning filling up with the locals and the tourists. She walked along the broad main street, looking into all of the shop windows. There were shoe shops and clothes shops, shops with lots of knick knacks and mementos of this area and lots of restaurants, all kinds of restaurants. She smelled that smell again. The one she'd caught at breakfast although she hadn't had any bread. The smell of fresh baking. She realised she was starving and sat down outside a café, ordering a cappucino and some fresh croissants. The waiter was friendly and, of course, spoke English. She asked him about the church and the fresco.

"Ah, yes. Well, there is a story, Signora. The church is called Santa Maria a Mare and it is called this because a wooden icon of the Madonna was found in the sea here. It is still in the church. The Madonna has saved our sailors many times. The fresco shows her saving yet another ship of sailors from harm."

An American couple sitting near her were talking about the town. He was looking at a guide book, reading the information aloud.

"It is one of the few towns on the coast with a beach. It says we landed here during the war. Hey, did you know that there was an earthquake here in the fifties and they had to rebuild their seafront completely. That is why we are sitting here in this wide street. The Corso Reginna was built as part of the redevelopment after the earthquake."

Nessa felt overwhelmed by all of this information. In Italy, even in a small town like this, there was so much history, so many layers of civilisation that it was hard to take it all in sometimes. She decided to take a walk further along the seafront to clear her head. The road narrowed considerably and it was becoming dangerous to walk along. She turned back. Before deciding to be brave and face Rosa again, she looked out at the calm, blue sea and realised that she hadn't thought about Joe or her job or her future for at least an hour, if not longer. That had to be a good start. Immediately she began to feel better. She would get over things and she would move on. She just had to immerse herself in the here and now. She would heal and the future would fall into place for her. She bought a guide book in a small shop across the road from the promenade and found, to her delight, that there was the remains of a Roman villa about a mile away in what had to be a smaller town called Minori. She would go back to the *pensione*, have lunch and make her way there. She could feel her heart lifting slightly. Even that slight lift felt like a small miracle to her. And small miracles were all she had. For now.

Bed and Breakfast
Bernie Furlong

It was after ten o'clock that evening when they arrived in Dublin on the last train. Dolores wished that they had left home earlier but her father had been working and didn't want to miss a day's pay. Now it was too late to go out to UCD and she wouldn't be able to enrol until tomorrow. They got off at Pearse, the station that her father still insisted on calling Westland Row. On Pearse Street they stopped at a three-storey house with a sign for bed and breakfast. The front of the house was grimy and uncared for and looked uninhabited. Its brick façade was coated in a film of grey soot. Dolores could just make out tattered net curtains in the windows. A rectangular cardboard sign hanging slightly askew in the window nearest the door stated bleakly - VACANCIES.

Her father pressed the bell and Dolores heard a muffled jangling noise coming from inside. There was a shuffling sound and the door opened slightly, leaving just enough room for a woman's face to appear.

"Do ye have a booking?" She did not seem surprised when Dolores' father shook his head. The door opened wider. "Have ye a room for two. A double?" her father said. The woman hesitated.

"I mean, a… a two bed room!" He said, his face reddening. He wore that expression that always made her uneasy. Defensive and unsure in equal measures. His chip-on-the-shoulder face as she always thought of it. The woman was wearing a stained blue nylon overall. She had drawn a fat line of frosted pink around her mouth and two surprised crescent moons of brown above her eyes. A dusty cobweb of a hairnet covered her thin grey hair. She shuffled down the dimly lit hall towards a reception desk covered in chipped brown Formica.

"Ten pound a night for a twin. Breakfast is included."

She handed Dolores' father a large key with a dangling tag.

It seemed even darker inside the house than outside, as though light had never managed to penetrate through the filmy windows. Dolores could barely make out the woman's rounded back as she climbed the stairs ahead of them. Lamps shaded with pink tasselled plastic hung at intervals along the wall but did little to illuminate the gloom. There was a stale fried food smell that made Dolores queasy. At the top of the stairs another corridor stretched ahead, identical to the one below. The woman pointed.

"Number 19 on the left. Toilet is at the end."

In the room, two single beds, each draped with identical faded green candlewick spreads, sat uncomfortably close together. Yellow light from a street lamp seeped through the curtain. Dolores looked in the mottled mirror on the washstand. Her skin had a yellowish hue. The new fringe she had liked so much last week hung flat like beagles-ears against her temples.

"This isn't too bad." Her father said. But he frowned as he pulled back the bedclothes.

Dolores drew aside the net curtain and looked down onto the street. It seemed oddly deserted, as though the city was under curfew. A soggy front page from the Evening Press lay disintegrating in the gutter. The excitement and hope that had been bubbling up inside her on the journey was beginning to evaporate.

"We could go out. Have a look around," she said, hoping something could be salvaged from a day of disappointment. Her father didn't reply. He was still inspecting the room and was now investigating the wobbly wardrobe, peering inside, opening and closing the door, checking the hinges. There probably weren't many places open anyway except pubs and she didn't want her father drinking. She decided to get ready for bed instead.

She couldn't find the light switch in the corridor and had to feel her way towards the bathroom, touching the flock wallpaper as if it were Braille. She passed two more doors with light coming from underneath and heard muffled voices. A man's voice and then a woman's, speaking so quietly she could not make out what they were saying. There was a sudden burst of high brittle laughter and then silence again. The bathroom smelled of Jeyes Fluid and damp. Dolores stood on tiptoe and peered through the small barred window. The railway line was a few feet away. An empty train passed suddenly, making the walls vibrate and pushing a gust of sooty tasting air inside. She washed her face and shook some talcum powder into her hair, brushing it through. Checking the mirror again she realise this hadn't make her hair less greasy as she had hoped. Now it was just duller and greyish, clinging to her scalp like a felt hat.

In bed the sheets were clammy. She could not bear to rest her cheek against the pillow and placed one of her tee-shirts over it. She lay flat and corpselike under the covers, reluctant to move, watching the passing of every hour on the luminous dial of her travel alarm clock. Her father snored in the bed beside her as she watched the sweeping lights of passing cars reflected on the wall. She tried to think about starting college the next day, but she couldn't imagine anything beyond this night. Every so often a train rattled by, making the house shudder, before it settled back again into silence and darkness. College was still just an image, a glossy photograph of a modern building beside a man-made lake, and no matter how hard she tried she could not will herself into the picture.

all
good things
begin

on the way

Going Home.

Thomond Gill

Presents packed, pride
I think, the feeling
Of an adult return
(train not bus) ticket marking
A new chapter in my
Battered green book
shaky on the table

My hands around the paper cup
Comforting the early morning fog.
Thick in the heavy air
are promises of a sunny few days.
Last nights, and older, sleepy dreams
Chugging in my mind

As a train on another platform
begins its journey to a known destination
that feeling of 'are we moving?'
still felt the confusion of a child's
Inability to trust sensations.

The blurry green trees the
sleeping cows and tunnels.
Crickety motions and in my mind
no deadlines, exams or longing
for a home cooked meal

but a rattling I can't make out.

The Full Seven

Christina Park

"I have an appointment …with death."

Rob had been saying it last night, in his deepest movie trailer accent, to anyone from the office who'd listen. Images clinked past at a nauseous tilt, in live action colour: the black tiles of the bar, slivers of mirror behind, in which he would catch a glimpse of himself when he went to order; the lights picking out his ski tan so it looked false, though you could still see the hint of the panda eyes he'd picked up – white, not black – from wearing the goggles and no sunscreen. A newly shaved head covered the receding hair issue. Ballsy with the suit, he thought. I like it. He rubbed the stubble behind his ear and called for four pints and a whiskey and coke.

"Make it a double," he said. Mona was the only one impressed by his announcement, who knew how impressed? No harm in covering bases.

"Bin there, done that, mate," said Carl, shrugging his shoulders. "Death's overrated." Probably the best part of the deal was being able to say things like that and have all eyes turn to you. Worth every penny. Of course, now that Carl and even Jack had done it, it was a handicap not to, showed you didn't have the bottle. He glanced over as Peter slurped from a pint that seemed far too big for his spindled white fingers.

"What was it like?" Mona had switched allegiance. He was sorry he'd bothered with the double. Carl tapped his nose.

"That's between me and my Maker," he said. "Bigger buzz than skydiving any day, though, I can tell you that."

Jack leaned past him, wafting hair product.

"Who you going with, Rob?"

"Lazarus."

"They're the best. I did the Jesus package. Three days, three nights."

Carl smiled, adult to child. "Yes, well they're good and safe, all right," he said. "I'd take a bit of a risk, or what's the point?"

Rob took out the Lazarus leaflet and carefully slapped it onto the wet table. "They're the only ones," he said, over an unexpected burp, "who do the full seven."

That shut them up. They sat staring as water oozed through the leaflet, darkening its famous icon – a view down the vortex of a tornado – and dissolving the words at the bottom: "The other side: Dare to know". Eventually, Carl cleared his throat.

"Insurance is a rip-off for that one," he said. Rob smiled benevolently, giving a pope-like sweep of the arms.

"Anyone you want me to contact while I'm there?"

"Well, my cat died... " Mona's voice was drowned in a wave of laughter. The table gave a dangerous wobble. Peter was pushing past everyone to get out.

"Hey, what's the face for, Peter? Hey Peter?" Jack shouted at the retreating back, then shrugged. "What's his problem?"

"Can't hold his drink for shit," said Carl. He swilled the flat end of his pint round the glass and downed it. "Who's for another?"

Rob snorted in his sleep. He tried to turn around but there was something behind him. The end of the night had broken up like an ice floe. Jack's place. Food fossilised on dishes by the sink. Trapped noodles and a white baked bean in the plug hole. Carl cutting the lines on the table. Sliding tongues, whiskey and coke, the shell of an ear.

He wasn't really asleep anymore, just clinging onto the dregs, trying to ignore his heart as it pumped a lowgrade electric buzz through his limbs. His teeth ached as if he'd been grinding again. Swallowing dryly, he opened one eye. And winced. A sharp javelin of sunshine stretched across the room, searing against the white floorboards. He became aware of a weight across his waist: an arm. His blood current gave a high voltage kick. Lifting the limp wrist, he twisted about and squinted behind. Mona. Shit. Acid swilled in his gut. A stranger would have been simpler.

The sliver of sun picked out her silver gypsy earrings and the goosebumps on her upper arm. Her mascara had slid, giving her closed eyes a Barbra Streisand droop and there were scars of old acne along her jaw. Still, she was pretty. With a shock, he realised he didn't care – about the prettiness, or the scars. He might as well have been observing the precise details of a plant or a cup. You cold bastard, he thought, disgusted. Pulling the duvet over her shoulder, he made to slip out of the bed. At the movement she twitched, kitten-like and snuggled towards him in her sleep. Animal warm. What the hell. It was his last day, after all. Leaning over shakily, he kissed her stale mouth, insisting until it loosened and began to taste good again, the feel of her full shape feeding the current pulsing through him.

"On the last day," his Lazarus consultant had suggested, "you will be overwhelmed by life's intensity, experiencing all those precious details as if for the first time."

Midday and Mona was at the kitchen table, pouring out cornflakes. Halfway through his last day. Her work blouse was crumpled, her face once again smooth and blemishless, a shade darker than her chest, her lips very bright pink. She got up and rummaged loudly in his cutlery drawer, taking out two spoons.

"You want some?"

He shook his head with care. Putting on the kettle, he stuck the cornflakes back in the cupboard. On the packet, below the list of ingredients, was typed in bold: "Recommended by experts as first breakfast after the Lazarus sleep".

Funny, how everything ended up on a cereal packet in the end.

When the whole phenomenon first started up, people used to go on chat shows and talk about fantastical experiences, a new sense of meaning. It used to take years off your life. It had only really hit the mainstream when psychiatrists had started prescribing "a trip down under" to overcome that niggling fear of death they termed necrophobia. Nowadays, as long as you passed the rigorous health check, they estimated death tourism cut only six to twelve months off your span – more like twenty for the seven days. But then, look how many people used to smoke, as Jack had pointed out. And how many years does that take off your life?

"Nice view you've got." Mona was looking towards the north bank over the opaque spasms of the Thames. It was high tide, so the bicycle wheel and various bits of rubbish stuck forever in the thick silt were covered over.

"Mmm, expensive view," he said automatically. This time tomorrow he would be dead. After the world trip, the drugs, the adrenalin sports, this was surely it. The biggest hit of all.

Mona ploinked her spoon into the bowl.

"Hey, what happened with Peter in the end? Did he get home all right?"

"Peter?"

"Yeah, you guys all dragged him out of the room. Don't you remember? He went completely beserk, raving about your Lazarus thing."

Rob shrugged. "Just cause he hasn't got the balls…"

"That's not fair, Rob." She pointed her spoon in accusation. "Don't you know he's not well…" she paused, flushing.

Rob looked up in surprise.

"He's what?" She looked sorry she'd spoken.

"Sarah from HR told me."

A tepid wash of guilt passed over him. "What do you mean, not well?"

"Nothing. Never mind. Don't tell anyone." She talked quickly to cover her tracks. "Just, well, you don't know what's on his mind... Or he might know someone who's died. I mean, would you be doing this if someone... I mean, don't you know anyone who's died?"

He supposed so, grandparents and the like. He could only recall one funeral. His mother's father. A sunny day like an overexposed photo, pine coffin and a sheet of faux grass covering the upturned pile of earth. It was like someone else's house that day, stuffy, full of strangers drinking tea and being sorry for his trouble. Bess was snuffling round the kitchen lino for crumbs, getting underfoot. So he'd grabbed her lead and they'd escaped through the woods, up past the blazing gorse to the other side of Crock Hill. There they'd explored crooked thistle-silver fields and the mysterious arched highways of hollow ditches until evening tightened the world around them and they had to go back.

Bess. A year later the vet had carried her out of the surgery in a black bin bag, a cartoon outline of dog, stiff like a prop. When they'd left her, she didn't cry. Only sat small and precise on the tiled floor, bronze coat in tendrils from running in the wet grass that morning. In the boot of the car he'd torn open the bag. It could almost still be her, if it weren't for the flat jelly eyes, the tongue jammed against teeth, the smell of soiling. Her coat was still drenched, organs detailed and pointless underneath.

The boiling kettle switched off with a snap. He tried to make his smile natural. "Died? Just the once you mean?"

She laughed and slapped his shoulder, relieved to be back on frothy ground. He took out the percolator. "Coffee?"

"Can you make cappuccino?"

In the end, he let Mona walk him part of the way to the appointment: along the river, past the Globe and the massive warehouse of the Tate Modern. Passing underneath Blackfriars Bridge, they were hit by the stench of urine. Further along a dark clot huddled in the gloom, a sleeping bag worm in foetal curl. Rob's breath quickened slightly as he passed by, but the form didn't stir.

"No, honestly, Embankment is the best station for me," she insisted, as

223

they crossed Waterloo Bridge. "So that suits you going onto the Strand." Her voice was drowned by a bus that drew past with the famous tornado ad raging on its side. A wild bluster blew her hair into her eyes and tossed pigeons around like paper bags, the April sun constantly sharpening and disappearing as though it were flooding and soaking into the ground. She stopped on the bridge and looked across the slug of dull scuffed water at Charing Cross Bridge. On the south bank, by the Royal Festival Hall, walkers scuttled past the secondhand book market, buffeted this way and that.

He tried to see everything anew, like the consultant had suggested, but it all looked the same: same bitch of a wind, same scurrying crowds, same leeching sky. Mona leaned towards him. She wanted him to kiss her, he supposed, so he did, lips cold from the wind, coats getting in the way of the embrace. She put her hand up to his face. This must be someone else, he thought, standing on the bridge with a girl touching his cheek. A scene from a film or another life. It meant something to somebody, maybe. He had to look in her eyes, like he knew her. They were hazel, he realised suddenly, very dark. He was itching to get away, away from the gaze, but found himself holding her hand to his cheek for a moment. He let go abruptly. Heading alone towards the Strand, he was aware of the ghost outline of her fingers on his skin, colder now than the rest of his face.

The waiting room resembled nothing so much as a retreat centre. Trees and waterfalls backdropped pithy little poems in curly type. In between, the wall's winter green was lit by carefully angled white canvas lamps. It was probably the tinkling of a taped fountain that made Rob want to go to the bathroom again. He resisted, fiddling in his pockets for something to distract him. He should have brought a book. A scrap of paper with Mona's number on it, his mobile and a stiff piece of card: his Death Insurance policy. He read the familiar blurb, under the heading: "There's never been a better time to die!"

He'd get his death cert when he came back round, next week. His body would go cold, and suffer rigor mortis, but the dry freezing meant it wouldn't decay. He'd seen Carl's video, even been to Jack's mock funeral. He knew what it looked like from this side. Now for the other. His consultant had hinted heavily that everyone who'd gone for the full seven days had had some sort of revelation. "Any shorter is just to take the sting out of death," he'd said dismissively, as he looked down at Rob's health stat sheet.

The room felt stuffy after the wind outside. He checked his mobile. No messages. Time: 17.45. Five minutes fast, according to the red hands of the plate-faced clock on the wall. He supposed he could put in Mona's number, just to kill time. She'd run down the steps at the north side of Waterloo Bridge, skirt plastered to the side of her leg with the gusts. At the bottom, she'd turned and waved, cheeks glowing through her foundation. "Give us a call when you rise from the dead."

"It's not a joke." He caught a flash of Peter's white face at Jack's. He was drunker than Rob, his eyes and lips shiny and wet. "It's not a fucking joke!" He used the word "fucking" as though it were a glob of phlegm he was trying to clear; his bony fingers pronged Rob's upper arm. "You make fun, yeah, you go on and make... fucking... fun."

Rob went to the toilet. A couple of desultory squirts into the funnel of the bowl. He avoided the mirror. Back in the waiting room, he propped himself on the edge of his seat, elbows on knees. His mobile was heavy in his pocket. He took it out. No messages. He put his hand to his cheek. Maybe he could write a quick one, no strings. A side door opened and a casually dressed woman passed through wafting a faint scent of disinfectant edged with burnt metal. As she opened the door to his left, he glimpsed a fluorescent strip of light, surgery bright.

"You make fun, yeah... You go on and make ...fucking ...fun."

The door opened. The consultant smiled, stranger to stranger.

"Right," he said. "Are we ready?"

Homeward Bound

Anne O'Donoghue

Grace closed her eyes as the plane accelerated down the runway and the nose lifted. She felt the tension leave her muscles as the force pushed her back in the seat. She felt the corners of her mouth widen and the length of her brow extend. She closed her eyes and fell still. This was always her favourite point of the journey, travelling home, or perhaps more precisely to some notion of home. Being on a plane seemed to allow some licence as to the detail of the destination, as if at this great height you might pick up another thread of existence and be transported to another reality, like getting a crossed wire on a telephone call. She let her head fall to the side to see the world at an angle. The whole world shrinking away and losing its pull. Everything made more sense from a vertical distance. Things seemed to move more gently and everything seemed better placed somehow. Villages looking like dents on a decorative metalwork piece – bashed through the skin of the earth from behind in dots. The crazy paving fields and the occasionally distinguishable barn placed on a lattice of green like a Monopoly piece. And then the engines go quiet as the plane flattens out like its trying to tiptoe through people's back yard mindful of the disturbance. This was a place where normal rules didn't apply and she could breathe easy in the knowledge that she could have no influence on progress. She didn't even like declaring a preferred seat when asked at check-in. She liked to hand over all decision making power with her passport. She felt at ease now cradled in tin, suspended between worlds.

The trip had been short and not really necessary. The invitation to give a guest lecture on her research to a group of first-year science students in Scotland came from a longtime friend who probably felt the break might be a good idea. If Sarah's call had come directly to her she would have declined but Sarah had gone to straight to Tim, who insisted. Sarah and Tim had been flatmates for years and were still capable of hatching conspiratorial plots. Grace tried to pan the whole thing, but he with a wry smile said, "Look, I know I'm not in great shape but I intend to be here until the weekend anyway". And then his attempted chuckle made him crumple and gasp and reach for the oxygen mask. This was the time where they struggled to find conversation. They were now separated by the disease. Originally when the diagnosis was made they examined it from the outside, researched it, analysed it and its implications like a kind of macabre joint project. They started a file, like when they had been decorating the house and the choice of wood flooring became a decision backed up by a spreadsheet and a fully indexed file of primary and secondary research. But now that time had passed and Tim was in the clutches of something she could still only see from the outside. And it was harder for them to find a meeting place. There was no resentment on his part, or if there was he hid it flawlessly, but there was an insurmountable presence between them. She missed him already. He was occupied by drugs and chemicals that eased his pain but drowned him out. She resented that. She could accept them being shortchanged on time – as if she had a choice – but found it harder to cope with the savagery of the compromises imposed on the time they had. Now he required the oxygen full time and she knew he hated the presence of medical equipment in their home. It was a marker that they were losing ground, on every level.

She had delivered the lecture by rote. It was a complete mismatch with the audience but that didn't matter. They sat there anyway, doodling away the hour. Her specialist field was 'The Life Cycle of the Freshwater Eel'. In fairness a bit of a stretch in terms of immediate relevance for this kind of slot. But Sarah said her view as a Senior Lecturer of the Department was that it was "essential that these students were exposed to the real work of real science practitioners". Then she laughed and said that if it so happened that such a practitioner happened to be a friend that she hadn't seen in an age, then she was prepared to overlook that fact too, for the sake of their education. "And anyway so what if it is not relevant. How often do you consider the implications of String Theory when tagging a baby eel? But I don't recall anybody apologising to us for making us take that module to get our degree."

There was a girl in the front row who began to distract her as the hour went on. The kind with three different coloured biros placed in a neat row exactly parallel with the top of her writing pad. She drew lines under the headings she had written in neat small caps at the top of the page. For a while Grace thought she was genuinely interested but as the hour went on her expression changed. At first she looked a bit confused but as Grace went deeper into her data her expression changed to one of moderate indignation and then mild alarm. As if it was downright rude and unfitting to be confronted by such volume of information – unseemly quantities of scientific fact being exposed. Her expression was vaguely comical. Grace wouldn't have registered boredom or apathy, that sensor was long since disabled, but the indignation was downright funny. For the first time in weeks she had an impulse to laugh – heartily. She smiled now as she thought of it. And then broke into a sudden hard laugh placing her earphones over her ears and turning her face to the window to escape the curious glances.

The plane was turning. She really loved this bit. The plane quite steeply angled and pivoting on the point of the wing below her. It reminded her of an image she carried in her mind since her time in Greece. She had spent a considerable amount of her time there pushing her scooter uphill to the local mechanic's house to have it resuscitated. He was a big even-paced man who seemed to charge her very little for his ministering. She knew he did some windsurfing but one day saw him out on the waves and could not believe how light and athletic he was on the board. He was in the distance, moving across the glistening water dancing round the sail – it was balletic. And that's how she thought of the plane now turning elegantly on a point. She wondered if it was necessary to dip so much or if the pilot chose to move that way because it was more graceful. She hoped so, she hoped that sometimes he looked out the window and saw what she saw. Sporadic patches of forest – knobbly looking. Like the fuzzy patches that grow on a favourite jumper.

There was a toddler in the second row growing fractious. He was past being bored, past being mollified, he was escalating his protest to a full unfettered bawl. He yelled repeatedly in long rasping howls so that you could hear the rawness inflate his throat. He paused only to catch his breath. The pitch of it made her skin prickle. And yet she envied him the freedom, the luxury to protest in such an unqualified manner even if there was nothing to be gained. The world was at least aware of his feelings as they were, unchecked, untempered and in their full veracity.

When she was staying at Sarah's for the night she woke a 4 o'clock to hear someone screaming in much the same way as the second row bawler. She eventually got up as the episode went on. She couldn't see anyone but she could hear the kicking of a door and the plaintive demands for entrance. It was a very cold night. It sort of shocked her. It would have been less shocking to hear screams of terror, that would be within the range of normal in terms of prescribed adult responses. But there was no terror in this only rage and frustration. She figured that there had been an argument, maybe initiated by allegations of flirting with the barman by a jealous boyfriend who stormed home and locked the door leaving his girlfriend exiled in minus three. It was still quite something to wail in the way she did. It could not be ignored. Eventually it stopped. And as the lights in the apartments were flicked off and people turned back on to their pillows she wondered if there were really only two kinds of people in the world – those who open their throats to cry out in protest and those who bite down on their own screams. Those who give vent to the pain sing it out like an errant note into the universe and those who chew on it attempting to shred it into bite-sized pieces to be digested whole.

The seatbelt light went on. The descent began. It was time to consider her mood. Lately she found herself pausing in doorways to check or change her mood, as you might select the appropriate clothing for an occasion. She was getting better at it. The key was selecting a mood she could sustain. No point in putting on a Holly Golightly expression going into a Department meeting if you were seen to be surreptitiously searching the bottom of your bag for a tissue by tea-break. And so it was with going home, she would take a reading from the air of what was needed and adjust her settings so that she strolled through the door emitting some kind of balancing note. Though it wasn't what she had ever imagined for them, she was glad to be back home now – on any terms.

Slippy Water

Clare Farrell

She liked slippy water
that's what she said
on holidays in Dublin
and everyone laughed.

She liked to drink it
in large quantities
and to wash in it
feel the soap bubbles
burst out soft on her skin
and the slippy water
slide down the groove
of her back in the bath.

When she got older
she liked to swim in it
to glide along the surface
and feel it wash over her
as she cut through
in easy freestyle.

Swimming through slippy water
sometimes at breakneck speed
not stopping for breakfast
she passed buses on her way to work
three strokes and up
on alternate sides for breath
before going under again
to join the slippy water.

And commuters smiled
and waved and watched her go
overtaking cars and bikes
and plunging under for traffic lights
for fear she'd lose her pace.

Then one day she
slowed to floating on her back
and buses passed her by
and passengers grinned sadly
and angry drivers swerved
to miss her
and a little pool of slippy water
filled her belly button
spilling out a sorry
single trickle down her skin
as she floated out to sea
non-stop
heading home
on the tide of slippy water.

The Eighth Blunder

Cal Daly

He said I shouldn't be so hard on myself, that I should think of myself less like the kid who always got picked last and more like the team captain. He said I was far too redundant in my own life and needed to be more confident and assertive. He said he would help me every step of the way.

He said, "Why do you do yourself the injustice of thinking yourself unimportant?"

He said I thought of myself as "just" myself, "only" me, always compromised. And he said as long as I did, then that's who I'd be.

He said, "Is that who you want to be, Madeline?"

"No sir I said…I don't think so…I guess not…no…no."

"No?" he said.

"Yes," I said.

"Yes?" he said. "Did you say yes?" he said.

"Oh no I said… I had said no and then you said no so I was agreeing and saying yes to your no."

"You see Madeline?" he said.

I did, I saw. He went on.

He said there were two types of people.

"There are planet people and there are world people. There are those people who think themselves inferior and therefore are. They think they are lesser parts of a greater whole. The world does not revolve around them, they revolve around the world; passive, submissive, victims, routine. They are planet people. Then there are those who know themselves superior and therefore are. They know they are omnipotent, in command of themselves and everyone and everything around them. They know the world revolves around them; aggressive, dominant, extraordinary. They are world people."

He said, "Which one are you Madeline?"

I couldn't win. If I said planet I was a loser and if I said world I was a liar so I thought fast and told him what I hoped he wanted to hear.

"I don't know sir but I do know which one I want to be."

"Which one Madeline?"

"World," I said. "I want to be the world."

I heard myself say it and hated myself even more.

"Great," he said.

"Fantastic," he said, he bellowed.

"Well let's get you started. Let's try something," he said.

"You say you want to be a world person."

"Yes," I said. And I meant it... I think.

"Well Madeline, there are seven wonders of the world. And if you really want to be the world then you have to believe you are and that means you have to believe you have seven wonders about you," he said.

"Seven," I echoed, like a planet.

"Seven," he said, like the world.

"We've done so much today," he said, "so much, so I'll leave you with this."

He said I had to stop thinking of myself as the eighth thing on a list of seven, forever on the cusp, the one no one bothers with and move myself on to the list, be the list.

"For next week," he said, "what I want from you, for you, is your list. Tell me, but most of all tell yourself, your seven wonders."

The whole point of seeing this guy was to try to counter my low self-esteem. But six into the seven days he had given me to come up with seven good things about myself I had nothing. This was working wonders. On the seventh day, I was not even close to having created my world, so unlike God, I could not rest. I found myself in my room in a sea of drafts that read more like childhood first confessions than assured promise of greatness.

1. I am good to my parents.
2. I pray daily.
3. I will go to confession to seek forgiveness for lying in 1 and 2.

> I will endeavour always to be good to my parents.
> I will endeavour always to pray...oh God help me!

I had soul-searched until it was soul-destroying. I had even Googled myself and unless I'd forgotten I'm a Canadian herbalist specialising in natural remedies for memory loss, even that proved futile. When put to it, I struggled to come up with one concrete positive attribute that was either true or believable. It wasn't that I kept coming up with drive-by shootings and stolen cars. I'm a good person. But in terms of Dr Mike's analogy, if

I'm honest, I am absolutely a planet person. In fact, I'm probably more accurately described as an undiscovered moon that orbits a planet person. I'm so far away from being a world person, I'm in a whole other galaxy. But he said I had to do the list, and if for no other reason than preserving what little self-worth and respect one has going to a motivational therapist working from his mother's living room, I was determined to come up with seven things I liked and thought likeable about myself. Seven things... just seven... only seven... Jesus seven?

I kept thinking I must have come up with something in six days. I checked and re-checked endless drafts that weren't even beginnings. Of course there were some things there, some qualities, some ideas but they were tragically ordinary. The person in those drafts was good, no doubt, but it was a basic goodness and a basic person with no hint of potential to ever be anything more. I was stumped. It seemed the only thing I was good at was being ordinary. Then just as I was about to give up and give in to my mediocrity, I thought, well maybe that's it. Maybe that's my list. You have to go with what you know. Some people know quantum physics, I know mundane and apathy. Maybe what I had going was a refreshingly honest self-acceptance. I had after all been able to concede to myself that I was 'only' a planet person. I had enlisted myself for therapy, and they say admitting the problem is halfways to solving it. And I had torn up page after page of wonderful wonders because I knew they were wonderless lies. So I took up a clean sheet and started writing.

1.   I am an extremist in a petty way. It's not all or nothing in terms of conquering Everest or the world or my fears; rather I will veer between not tolerating a crumb on my kitchen surface and eating bread off the floor.

2.   I hate the rain. I can bear pretty much any other weather but I find rain relentless. It brings out the worst in me. Sometimes I cry too much, and in the rain no one can tell. It depresses me and makes me horribly pensive so that when I get caught in a really bad rainfall I stop hating the rain and start hating myself.

3.   I have no idea what my natural hair colour is. Baby photos tell me I am a brunette but childhood photos enlighten me. I have been blonde since I could afford it.

4.   I think too much and do too little. Even now in saying that I think too much and do too little I am conerned as to how you will react to my telling you that I think too much and do too little. Will you agree fervently and so disregard what I have to say because you know it will

merely serve to confirm that if this is all I have to say and all I have to do is say it then I am absolutely right when I profess that I think too much and do too little?

5.   I am not a gossip and to that end only gossip as much as the next non-gossip. Curiosity, whilst being of the most basic human instincts, also compels us to commit the most callous acts of disloyalty. I however am utterly trustworthy. If you tell me a secret I will not betray your confidence. Except to Emma of course, I tell her everything. There are two exceptions, two things I will never tell.

6.   I find it difficult to understand and impossible to empathise with people who wear odd socks. If, as adults, we can not govern that simple part of our lives then what hope is there? By adhering to the following simple procedure you can ensure that you never end up with odd socks.

6.a   Owning three pairs of socks when there are seven days in the week and a maximum of two washings per week (realistically and practically speaking) does not help one's chances of maintaining a healthy sock stock. It is imperative then that that you own at an absolute minimum seven pairs of socks. Ideally one should own twenty-one pairs which allows three weeks before your sock stock is exhausted. This covers all eventualities in terms of unexpected illness or two concurrent weekends spent travelling, anything which may act as a conspiratorial preventative to regular washing.

6.b   Assign yourself a sock-drawer. This is the only place your socks will be and only socks will be there.

6.c   After purchase, socks are balled and placed in this drawer.

6.d   Each day one pair is removed from the drawer for wearing and each night it is balled and placed in the laundry basket.

6.e   After washing, socks are dried, balled and returned to their drawer.

7.   I like my own company, not all of the time, only some of the time, just now and then. If I'm feeling tired at the end of a trying day, sometimes I just don't have the energy to be with anyone else. Sometimes even the thought of interaction can be exhausting and it's just easier to be alone. It can be unexpectedly comforting to have quality me-time; to sort out my room, my wardrobe, my washing, my head. There's a point at which spending time alone becomes the only company you crave and the best company you have.

It has only just occurred to me that maybe it is this point on my list that breeds the first six.

As had happened during composition, reading my list now to Dr Mike had caused me to drift off, on this occasion to the point that I was no longer aware of anyone else being in the room. Forgetting myself, and then remembering not to, I lifted my eyes from the page, expecting to be met by his, wild and engaged and hanging on my every word. Instead I realised he too had drifted off, wishing he was anywhere but in the room. His eyes were shut tight and his mouth wide open as every ounce of his being poured into the huge yawn he was only half way through. Only when the new and welcomed silence notified him that I had stopped speaking did he stop yawning.

"Interesting," he said, "interesting indeed."

"A first draft perhaps," he said, feigning pathetically knowledge of a single word I'd said.

And then he paused. He leaned forward, offering me the last biscuit. At some stage during my list his mother had delivered the complimentary tea and biscuits offered if you pay for ten sessions in advance. Incidentally, this had not influenced my decision in selecting Dr Mike, which was just as well. I had taken tea the first week. They use leaves. They do not use a strainer, a fact I discovered only after my last overly-ambitious mouthful. I declined politely thereafter. And I declined again now. I let him have my last biscuit satisfied it would be just that. He ate it immediately relieved by the extra twenty-six seconds he did not have to speak for. Not that there was anything more to say. Though he would never know it, Dr Mike had earned his money. Having bored him practically to sleep, I realised there was literally nothing more this guy could do for my self-esteem. My list had proved a waste of time for him, but not, and surprisingly so, a waste of time for me. It was not necessary that he shared my new-found enthusiasm.

There was no way back from his pained 'interesting' remark, so I stood and readied myself to leave, preferring to save the both of us from his attempting to add any further and equally futile comment. Buttoning up en route to the door, I noticed it was raining. Hey, sometimes it rains. Knowing I wouldn't be back I threw a parting glance in Dr Mike's direction and saw his Mom return to the living room for the cups and plate, pausing before she headed for the kitchen to wipe crumbs from her son's lap. She must have been proud I thought, having a son a doctor.

Skimming Stones

Maresa Sheehan

Flat and rounded with an edge:
it stands out from the mound.

Skimming the surface is a skill:
it's all in the wrist.
The stone must be flat and rounded,
the stance low with a curvy bend.

Skim One is awkward and splashes
strobe lighting on drunken eyes
over the stone lids a corner kiss
"time to go, now, please!"

Skim Two hits a ripple passing
cars lighting up dashboard eyes
assured with a destination splaying
water like fingers on a knee.

Skim Three dips beneath the gleam
liquid hands on its back skimming
sideways for a while
then loosing
wings and finding feet.

Tick Tock

Kate Neil

The clock is ticking
In the quiet kitchen
Soon it will strike the hour

They seem quite unconcerned
Am I the only one who is aware
The clock is ticking

'You worry too much,' they say but
I'm sure it's getting louder
Soon it will strike the hour

Still they sit, lost in triviality
Not caring about how fast
The clock is ticking

It's trying to tell us
That time is slipping away
Soon it will strike the hour

The ice is melting
The seas are rising
The clock is ticking
Soon it will strike the hour.

Sacré Coeur

Eoin Cavanagh

Marjorie leant against the flatbed truck, chewing a plum from her handbag for energy. Sam Billingham, and his middle son, Rodge, were picking through the charcoaled detritus of her fire.

She stood on a piece of land known as Stoke Strip, on the margins of the fenlands. Her half-acre. When she'd first come to England, she had tracked down her grandfather's brother. He had introduced her to The Parcel, and the sliver of land on it which he owned. She had fallen in love with it, and bought a plot in the end, complete with its mobile home.

It was her haven. She got up there at least once a month. London's crowded tubes, its shopping arcades packed like elevators, they were alien to her. She was a South Islander; she had learned not to tell Londoners that she came from 'near Big Rock.' She had made the absolutely necessary repairs: the broken windows, the leaky roof. She had big plans for the place, but demands of life in London had always got in the way before.

She rubbed her belly, then ruffed her overcoat, hoping the bump would not show. Sam left his son sifting through debris and peeled off his heavy-duty gloves as he approached her.

"I reckon one load will do it, Mrs Marriot."

Mrs Marriot. Soon again to be plain Marjorie Slipvine. Rodge was hoiking layers of burnt chipboard panelling onto the truck. Strong lad, well built, biceped. Something glistened about his head. "Is that an earring he's wearing?"

Billington tut-tutted. "You can't say aught to kids."

"It must be hard."

"It'll be harder for him from here out. The idiot got some tart from Norwich up the spout. Going to be a Daddy. He can't even wash his own face, let alone a baby's. If he's looking to Granny and Grandad to feed and change the little bugger... "

At least the little bugger would have Uncles and Aunties and Granny and Grandad nearby. Marjorie fixed on her party smile. She was good in crowds, great even. It was one-to-one conversations she struggled with. Especially dates.

Sam hurried over to help his son with a crate over-full of wreckage. In heaving it on the truck they bumped it. A heavy object, about the length of her palm, dropped to the ground. Curious, Marjorie squatted to the dirt-road surface and picked up the fallen object. As she thought, it was a cast-iron paperweight Eiffel Tower, a souvenir of a pre-honeymoon trip to Paris, where she and Clive had spent a long weekend in a *pension* in a Montmartre side street. It rained and rained. They went out twice: once for the Louvre and once for Sacré Coeur. Happier times.

Apart from an inch at the bottom of one spur, the paperweight was completely blackened. She picked it up, afraid it would burn, as if it could retain the heat of the fire they had set that June day, three months ago. Liz-Anne, her best friend, had rung her, rushed: "I'm really sorry. Timothy can't make it. He's flying to Singapore, for a Monday meeting. He's in the air already."

Marjorie remembered the rush of annoyance, nearly panic: she had to do it that day. God knew when she would next get a Saturday off. She wondered about trying to do it on her own. That would be a last resort, a bit too risky. She went through the list of her other friends' husbands and boyfriends. Linda's Mike would have been perfect, but the pair were touring Caithness and Sutherland. She even thought of ringing Nigel, a thirty-two year old insurance underwriter she had had an abortive date with two weeks before. Too early for any kind of date. And he was boring. And the more boring he was, the more nervous she became.

But she could not imagine spending another night in the ruststained box in the state it was in. She dialled, automatically, her fingers typing out the number she did not want her brain to register. With every ring she was on tenterhooks, hoping he would not answer, poised to hang up.

"I'm at the Strip. You anything on today?" Clive's voice tenored between concern and overdone nonchalance. "Marj. Hello." He seemed surprised she had rung, though he had told her to call if she needed help with anything. Bring paraffin. While she waited, she poked around inside the mobile home. It was already heating up with the morning; the place gave off its usual musty odour. She filled a bucket from the outside tap and started wiping the Formica surface, until she realised the pointlessness of it. What could a forensic scientist, or a paleo-dustologist, deduce from the smears, the microparticles, the scabs and scars on the fold-out table? Did the structure record the good times and the sorrows, or was it unperturbed by the mini-dramas it had hosted?

She smoked out the window. She loosened the window fittings with her Allen key. The sun burst through; it became too hot to sit inside.

She listened to the fens: buzzing insects, hooping waders, rustling in the grasses. She heard the hum of his car tyres before she saw his dark-blue BMW, very stockbroker belt, very him. He was beaded in perspiration, giving out that the air-conditioning had given out. German engineering.

She had been wondering what it would feel like to be near him again. Of course she had. Their last weeks together had been the dull bruise which followed the body blow. At home, in the small hours, after a night with Triona and Simon, Gordon and Annie – his friends – he had overfilled her whisky. When he told her he wanted a divorce, she slammed the glass against the wall, spraying amber liquid all over. Pause for breath. Leaving her for Fiona, an old flame, mother of two, someone she used to joke with him about, after they were married. When the shock hit her, she ran out. He tried to stop her, they scuffled over car keys on the crazy paving – she was in no state to drive anywhere. As he grabbed her elbow, she felt oddly liberated. At that moment, for once, neither of them cared what the neighbours thought. She resisted the urge to hit him. He would not have minded, she knew that. Might even have assuaged his guilt. That happened in the small days between Christmas and New Year. They agreed amicable. They agreed what the solicitor called a 'clean break'. She hated the term, it made her think of a snapped femur.

He got out of the car wiping his forehead, sunglasses on. How long had it been? Five months, she worked out. He had moved out mid-January; apart from a few uncomfortable semi-negotiations, in the weeks immediately after, they had managed to avoid each other. He grinned at her, ducking like a naughty child who had been caught red-handed. Was he checking her out? Bastard. She felt like finding something to give out to him about, but he had made good time up here. And he was doing her a favour, after all. They circled warily, two tropical fish in the same tank. He reached his hand out to shake, she felt awkward and brushed her lips against his cheek instead.

"What's the paraffin for?"

"A bonfire." She gestured towards the rust-coloured structure. He was reluctant, crabby, cagey. She had to work to convince him. That was one side of him she would not miss. "Everyone does it. It's beyond repair."

He relented. "If you're sure." He checked the place in and out for anything dangerous. They took the fridge out, moving it by pivoting around its feet until it was beside the road. "That has to be disposed of properly," he said. She bit her tongue.

"Windows," she said. "I believe they blow out otherwise." She tossed him the Allen key and helped with the lifting, stacking the windows neatly off to one side.

He pulled two cans of paraffin out of his boot, then they backed both cars away, just in case. He was good at this kind of thing. His shirt collar was grimy though. He always left them on a day too long.

"A cuppa before we start?" she asked. She had brought a flask, and drank out of the top herself, and found a chipped cup in a press for him. They sat at the table. It was stiff. There was a knack to folding it out, it was becoming harder every time. Clive explored the interior, every nook, but avoided her eyes. She listened to the buzz of the fens, closer now with the windows removed. Clive pulled open a press; paperbacks, vacuum-sealing Tupperware containers and high-impact plastic dinnerware avalanched to the floor. He picked up the Eiffel Tower paperweight.

"Is this for the pyre too?" She nodded. "Don't you want it?" Was that a glimmer of disappointment, or just acknowledgement?

"You can take it if you like."

"If you really don't want it."

"What will Fiona say?" she could not resist asking. His eyes narrowed.

"I don't live with her."

Yet, she wanted to say, but she regretted mentioning her name.

She was glad he had come today. Part of her drew a secret pleasure out of being with him, for a short while. Their past was a lock-box in her heart that she could never unpick. He fingered the legs of the paperweight, an accusing finger pointing up between them. "You should really keep this," he started. At the same time, she reached out to push it towards him. Their fingertips met on the table top, met and held. She was shocked by the surge of blood to her face, the rush, the physicality. It felt like a spark had passed through their touch, though she would never describe it like that to anyone. He was caught too in lust and hunger. They met half-way, eyes leading to lips. He gripped her neck and hair, pulling her to him. For so long their kisses had been crusted and unremarkable. There are always ten reasons for not doing something, and only one reason to do it. That was Liz-Anne's favourite quote, though Liz-Anne could find twenty reasons not to do something, and usually no reason to do it. They fell onto the narrow bed, Eiffel's folly clanking to the ground. They pressed each other close, violinists on the forward deck, after the iceberg had pierced the bulkhead.

The look in his green eyes mirrored her own, she was sure. She pushed her head away from his, long enough to ask "Shouldn't we take precautions?" She could see from the blank panic on his face that the precautions were in his house, two hours drive back to Essex. "What the heck, why change a winning formula?" This was not the time for irony. The deck toppled, the ship slipped into the icy water, but there were no screams of despair.

After, she drifted between sleeping and waking. A wasp buzzed in and out, as if enjoying the absence of the window pane. The bed was so small, moving was a combined operation. They held each other close, they had to.

She surfaced alone. He had his back to her, sitting on a chair, but she knew he was preening, cutting nasal hairs with a small scissors with curved tips he carried with him for that purpose. Funny the things that were once just annoyances now made her nearly ill with disgust. She threw her T-shirt on, tugged her jeans up, trapping their mingled sweat against her body, for the very last time, she presumed. There was no running water. She tried to rub her face down with her dry palms. The wall-mirror was fractured into egg-shaped facets. A hazel eye; a brown-blonde curl; a still-visible waist: the raw materials for a new life were there, if she could marshal them. Clive was still her husband – technically. She should not feel like a cheat for making love to him. In the year before the break-up they had done it, what, a handful of times? He owed her, look at it that way. Had she done it to get at Fiona? Part of her felt she had, but that was a train on a different track.

Clive sprinkled a last dash of paraffin in the front door, and Clive looked at her. Ineffable sadness? He never talked about his emotions; the only thing you could be sure of was, if he was feeling anything, it was ineffable. "I never thought it would go so wrong," he said. She counted to three in her head. On the one hand, he could still surprise her. On the other hand, what a thing to say. She had never thought it would go wrong, full stop. Perhaps if they had succeeded in having children. Then again.

"You ready?" She brandished the box of matches at him.

"It's your party." The stock line irritated her. Clive had taken such pleasure in telling people she organised parties for a living – "damn good ones too". Looking for some gesture of finality, she ripped down the chipboard sign, on which he had once lettered "Sacré Coeur" in coarse red paint. She chucked it inside, affecting nonchalance.

His only reaction was two short steps back from the door. She flamed the match. Whoosh. The pit of flame burned blue, the tip sunflower yellow. Sacré Coeur turned into a funeral pyre, a fitting tribute to the holiday home which had served herself and Clive well, and before them her grandfather and his siblings. She was sad, but it was how she had imagined it. Tongues of flames raced up the outsides, arcing and meeting up top. Clive did not normally smoke, but he took a cigarette too. He walked the perimeter, making sure nothing was being thrown out that would cause a grass fire. She told him the ground was too damp for anything to catch, but he persisted.

She was fascinated at how the mobile home yielded in the face of the heat. The chassis was heavily corroded, the structure was built of zinc and low-quality iron. The mound burnt with a low flame. Clive had long since thrown his cigarette butt onto it.

"You OK here?"

"Fine." They brushed lips against cheeks, him instigating this time, but it was courtesy only. He drove off, windows down, sunglasses on, blonde hair jostled by the wake of his acceleration.

The engine of the Billingham's flat-bed truck growled into life. Earringed Rodge shunted the truck into line, preparing their getaway. Sam was trying to convince her to take this one as a freebie. He had got a lot of business out of the company she worked for. She fished her cheque book out of her handbag. "Take a hundred."

"Don't be daft. A fifty then, if it'll keep you happy. I'll pick up something for my grandchild-to-be." Mrs M. Marriot was printed on the cheque. She ripped it out: the last one.

"Give my regards to Mr Marriot."

"I will." She felt a point in her handbag pressing against her ribcage. She did not want to be dishonest with Sam. "Clive and I are getting divorced." He was slotting the cheque into his back pocket. He looked up sharply, to see if she was serious.

"Sorry to hear that." He was uncertain, then recovered himself. "If I had known I would have brought Edgar. The eldest. Can't seem to get him settled." He winked, to be sure she knew he was joking.

"Thanks, but I have enough on my plate without another man in my life." Sam climbed in behind Rodge, waving goodbye. Billingham and Son pulled away in a haze of dust. She would tell Clive the news in a few weeks, when the *Decree Absolute* came through. She tossed her handbag, weighed down by the cast-iron miniature, into her car, but did not get in immediately. She surveyed the remains. They had done a thorough job, even taking the footing blocks. Sacré Coeur was just a dark patch on the bare ground on Stoke Strip, and memories.

Transported

James Stafford

The windows of the bus were misted with rain; inside, condensation streamed down the glass and the air was full of breathing and voices. The faces of the passengers flashed in reflection from window to window along the rows of houses and shops. I tried to catch sight of myself, but no two windows were on the same plane, or at the same angle, so that whenever I thought I recognised myself, we had moved on. Like a word that catches your eye in the newspaper; just for an instant, and then, it's gone. No matter how hard you look, even if you trace over the entire page with a pencil or the tip of your finger, you can't find it. A sign flashes on and off, but all your eye sees is the glow as the filament cools down.

An electrical shop had a window full of television sets, most of them tuned to game shows and rolling news. One of the screens was connected to a video camera that pointed directly out at the street. As the bus drew up alongside, so did my reflection. When it passed the screen the camera captured it and it seemed suddenly to change direction and double back. I turned away from the window – the reflected face was mine, but there was a stranger on the TV screen looking at me.

I wished the man beside me would move away. He took up too much of the seat, and I was aware of a smell that I could not identify. He was clean and shaved, but his life seemed to hang about him like a cloak. "Keeping busy?" he asked. I half-smiled an answer and concentrated on my paper, making sure that it was not open on a headline or anything else that might have started a conversation. "What do you do, yourself?" I became aware that I had not breathed in or out since he first spoke, and I made myself exhale softly. He was talking now to a woman across the aisle who had two small children. He took out a packet of sweets. He was now her problem, and I could lift my eyes.

I noticed that the bus had stopped moving. We were hemmed in by traffic, and I decided it had to be quicker to go on by foot. The driver shrugged, opened the doors without being asked, and I stepped out into the rain.

There was something in the street that I had to stand very still to catch. It could have been a smell or a sound, or even the memory of either of them, but I thought there was a piano in there somewhere, and an orchestra. It was not faint – it had to be loud to be noticeable above the traffic, but it was like an echo, that I was just half a second too late to catch. The man from the bus had got off just after me, and he heard it too. He nudged me with his elbow. "Remember Dusty?" he asked, "before your time, I'd say."

As soon as he spoke, it was obvious. I closed my eyes and it was the first time I ever heard it, on the radio in the garden; I remember that you were there. I felt that I needed to sit down or hold on to something solid. I had a big grin on my face, and there was a distinct possibility that I would be lifted off my feet, and be found at six o'clock in the evening, floating down the middle of South Great George's Street.

Gelsomina's Song

Yvonne Cullen

"La Strada," shot no.133: Gelsomina walks past a bare tree and stops to copy the angle of
its branches.

Old felt cloak and plimsolls Gelsomina
Gelsomina far from the sea
Trumpet and drum and road's apprentice

Fellini sets you down
Far away as a leaf could get from where you started
Where you're not loved.

Gelsomina no hope no home
Down the military road stretch your arms to love's width
Our shoulders itch to do it.

Gelsomina stand like a tree
Gelsomina keep on playing
All loss inside you like the marble's

Coloured twist,
Play everything that's lost,
Gelsomina sorrow.

Walk along with us: all strangers
True idiots inventing our way
Show us steps with the slow swagger of trumpets

That present the one we love
First one hip
Then the other-o

Be here so it's nearly funny in the sun
When we're sure again
We'll never have

The one we thought we'd found we wanted.
Gelsomina short fingers
Effort, sweetness. Always
Discovering: even a stone has a purpose.

Your trumpet's song:
A song a woman at sheets on a line sings
And says she learned

From a strange girl
Sings, and says she learned from a girl who
Was here, years ago.

For Giulietta Masina, actor, clown.

Split Ends

Helena Nolan

You know how country towns
Unravel out at their edges
The frayed hems of their outskirts
Trailing mud from the fields
The last light blinks
Before the road opens like a curl.
Sometimes at the very point
Where you have left
That final house behind you
There are two roads to choose from
Pitch-forked into the fields
Not a signpost in sight
And only the birds watching.
Often it's a decision
Made in faith
The size of the road or its shape
Suggests a destination.
Whatever happens you know
Its only a matter of miles
Before the next town
Shudders closer
Opening its thoroughfares in a yawn.
There will be other choices, other roads,
This isn't really an end –
Is it?

Notes

Foreword: Tomas Tranströmer quote: from Answers to Letters, Selected Poems of Tomas Tranströmer, Echo Press, New Jersey, 1987.

Magi: *"Behind the steering wheel sits..."*: Quote from radio broadcast by Robert Fisk.

Bavarian Dream: *Kleines Kopfkissen* is a small neck pillow.

The Last Wolf and the Last Woman Whose Mother Tongue was Cornish: This poem refers to two unrelated extinctions in 18th century Britain: the killing of the last wolf in Scotland, and the death of the last woman who spoke only Cornish. As the daughter of a bilingual father whose imaginative language was not that of his family, I thought of their isolation, and wondered what would have happened if the wolf had found his way to that woman's door...

A Grave at the End of the World: *Hecatomb:* an ancient Greek sacrifice of one hundred beasts.

Double Blades: A *Zamboni* is an ice resurfacing machine.

Guest-book: *Wachet Auf:* "Wake, o wake!": Bach Cantata BV 147

Gelsomina's Song: In Fellini's road movie *La Strada*, Gelsomina (Giulietta Masina) is the girl sold by her mother to Zampano, the circus strongman; a girl *"not like the other girls"*.

Biographies

Stephen Bailey was born in Dublin in 1976. He has written both fiction and non-fiction for the Irish Times and Village Magazine and has been a runner-up in the Davy Byrnes/James Joyce short story award. His favourite colour is blue. He is often lazy. He is currently living in West Cork and working on his first novel.

Deborah Ballard was born in London and now lives in rural Co. Carlow. She has worked as a solicitor, journalist, editor and film festival programmer and writes a monthly column for Gay Community News.

Barry Brown works as a Technical Specialist for a large software company. Born in Kerry, he grew up in Kildare and now lives in Dublin. He hopes to become a full-time writer once this computer fad passes.

Margaret Butler is from Dublin and studied English and History at UCD. She enjoys theatre and cinema and is an avid reader. She has been working in education for the last thirty-two years.

Eoin Cavanagh worked in Germany, Austria and Scotland before returning to Ireland in 1998. He lives in Bray, Co. Wicklow. He likes Thomas Pynchon but tries not to let it show.

Jody Collins moved to Ireland three years ago from Boston, Massachusetts. She now splits her time between Dublin and West Cork.

M.M. Cotter has one husband, two daughters, one full time job and many aspirations. These include (but are not limited to) being a writer, a better swimmer and a yogi. By inclination a slacker, she been unable to indulge in quality torpor for the last decade. In her spare time (of which she has none), she makes "to do" lists.

Cal Daly from Laois, having failed to realise her lifelong dream of being the first Laois Rose of Tralee, she resigned herself to writing. Her party piece is telling people that Laois is the only county in Ireland that doesn't touch a county that touches the coast. She doesn't get invited to many parties these days. She likes superheroes, short stories and to a lesser extent world peace. Some day she would like to write a short story about superheroes. In fact, when she grows up, she would like to save the world with a short story, a super short story

John Edmondson lives in Monkstown, Co. Dublin. He is a self-employed consultant to the financial services sector.

Clare Farrell grew up in Carlow and Monaghan, and now lives in Dublin with her partner and two sons. She is currently working full time on postgraduate research in sociology.

Conor Ferguson has been writing from an early age. His early work was predictably primitive – he wrote on walls, furniture and sleeping relatives – but his teens revealed a burgeoning gift for writing on copy-books and schoolbags. His writing today may be tainted with an inevitable, tedious orthodoxy, but his spelling isn't bad. He says, thanks for reading.

Mary Flynn Grew up in County Kilkenny and has lived in Dublin for many years. She worked as a Primary Teacher and was awarded an MA in Children's Literature from St Patrick's College, Drumcondra 2003. Her essay, Religious Literature for Children, published by the Talbot Press, was published by The Four Courts Press in 2004.

Bernie Furlong was born in England and moved to Ireland at the age of six. She discovered an interest in writing while completing an MA in Film where she was 'forced' to write several film scripts. Recently she has concentrated on writing short stories and is currently working on several interconnected pieces, which may eventually grow into a novel. She lives in Dublin.

Grace Garvey grew up in Glenamaddy, Co Galway, and now lives in Dublin. She studied law at Trinity College, before becoming a solicitor and later a journalist. She works as a sub-editor with The Irish Times.

Thomond Gill grew up on Inis Mór before moving to Dublin to college where she grew up some more. She is currently enjoying grown up life in Dublin but cannot decide whether her favourite colour is yellow or blue.

Mary Hackett lives in the Dublin suburbs. This is her first published piece.

Lori Johnston is Scottish and lives in Dublin with her boyfriend and two cats. She studied astrophysics at Trinity – all of it went over her head – and now works in education. She likes cats, hill-walking, and Porsches, and fears spiders. She is working on a collection of short stories.

Eileen Kavanagh was born in the Bronx and has lived for the last eleven years in Dublin. She is working on her first novel.

Ellie Madden was born in Sligo and now lives in Dublin with her husband and family. A busy woman, she still finds the time to write and is an active member of Off Centre Publishing.

Andy Maranzi is of Italian origin but has travelled extensively. He finally settled in Ireland fifteen years ago and works in the twilight area between arts and theatre. His first play, The Life Of Bran, has recently been performed to critical acclaim and he is currently researching his next project.

Samantha McCaffrey, lives in Dublin and is doing a masters in creative writing/fiction in Queens, Belfast, and very excited about it. Selected as part of Poetry Ireland's new poets' introductions series 2006.

Roisín McDermott grew up in County Down and now lives in County Kildare. She has an MA in English from NUI Maynooth and is published in the anthology of short fiction These Are Our Lives by The Stinging Fly Press.

Pat McGrath has been involved in sports coaching all of his adult life. Since retiring from active participation in sports he has taken to writing. He also has an interest in theatre, often assisting with stage lighting and occasionally treading the boards himself.

Marcella Morgan lives in Dublin and is working as a teacher. This is the first time she's been published.

Kate Neil was born in the UK and has lived and worked on West and East coasts of Australia and America, also in the Munich area of Germany. She has been settled in Dublin for some years now but still has itchy feet and dreams of far-off places... especially in Winter ...

Helena Nolan turned forty this year and decided it was time to take her work out from under the bed and show it to someone. She has since been short-listed for the FISH poetry prize and has been offered a place on the UCD MA in Creative Writing. She is married with two young sons, which is usually sufficient inspiration. She has lived in Kilkenny, Dublin, London and Kuala Lumpur.

Ainín Ní Bhroin lives in Dublin. She graduated from University College Dublin with a degree in Irish and English and worked for many years as a stage manager in the UK. She begins the MPhil in Creative Writing at Trinity College in autumn 2006. This is her first publication.

Órla Ní Chuilleanáin is twenty-five years old, and has been writing in her spare time for a number of years. She has taken workshops with Yvonne Cullen, Peter Sirr and Christian O'Reilly, and is now doing a full-time course in creative writing in Trinity. She is currently rewriting a first draft of a play about a dying workaholic looking back on his life, and beginning to write scenes for a novel she has plotted about a woman meeting an ex-lover after a long time apart.

Clodagh Ní Ghallachoir lives in Dublin. She was educated at Trinity College and Dublin City University. She is currently working on her first novel.

Nomleth Blackstar Nyapokoto is a young author and a poet originally from the Southern part of Africa. She got her inspiration from experiences in a foreign country. She uses poetry as her weapon to celebrate feelings and criticise the unjust.

Eobhan O'Brien was born in Co. Wicklow and has been living in Dublin for more years than she cares to remember. Eobhan currently works for Merchants Quay Ireland. Main weaknesses: white chocolate mousse and ginger beer – the latter due to excessive exposure to the Famous Five at an impressionable age.

Anne O'Donoghue lives in Dublin. She has no priors in publishing terms but has occasionally enjoyed reading a book, generally from the cosy side of a duvet.

Tim O'Halloran has worked in IT since he graduated from TCD. He lives in Finglas with his wife Jackie and family.

Paul O'Regan is a 30ish Dublin-born Software Engineer who's more Walter Mitty then Bill Gates. Making stuff up and travelling are his two favourite pastimes, procrastination being the demon of one and not enough holidays the other.

Christina Park Born 1972, studied English and history in TCD, before working as an English teacher in the UAE, Switzerland and Spain, and travelling through Europe, Asia, America and Africa. She is currently a sub-editor and travel writer.

Conn Redmond was born in Dublin City, raised in the seaside town of Rush, County Dublin, in the company of two great parents, one brother and several pets. Still wondering what to do when he grows up. In the meantime, writing, photography and travel occupy the in-between years.

V.B. Reid is a civil servant working and living in Dublin. He is a part - time painter, actor, musician, writer, footballer and carpenter. He is a firm believer that there is a thin line between a renaissance man and a "jack of all trades...".

Frances Plunkett Russell was born and lives on the Hill of Howth, having lived in the UK, USA, Germany, France and Scotland. She became a founder member of Peace '93 after the Warrington bombing of two children. Thereafter she became Programme Director of the Glencree Centre for Reconciliation. She holds an MPhil from Trinity College and is currently finishing a novel.

Maresa Sheehan born 1974 in County Cork. Currently hanging out in Dublin. Aiming to continue to improve at this poetry lark.

James Stafford was born in 1965 in Dublin, where he continues to scratch out an existence, usually managing to fly below the radar. He is currently a Piscean.

Joe Walsh is a sub-editor living in Dublin. His first short story, Fear, was published in 1977, in Young Irish Writing in the Irish Press, when he was seventeen. He then suffered 29 years of writer's block. One for the Road is his second published story.

Jenny Wright was born in Edinburgh and has settled in Dublin, so far.

Acknowledgements

We wish to acknowledge the generous support of the following sponsors

Bank of Ireland

Enniscrone Writers' Retreat

Anglo Irish Bank

Hooke & MacDonald

E.S.B.

Harney Nolan

The Westin Hotel

Meteor Mobile Communications

Waterfront House B&B, Enniscrone, Sligo

Easons

The Irish Writers' Centre

The Italian Alternative language school

Abbey Theatre

Sheries Café Bar

Photographer Jonathan Hunt

Chapter House Coffee Shop

Paula McGrath